SYMMETRIC SPACES

MATHEMATICS LECTURE NOTE SERIES

E. Artin and J. Tate	CLASS FIELD THEORY
Michael Atiyah	K-THEORY
Hyman Bass	ALGEBRAIC K-THEORY
Raoul Bott	LECTURES ON K(X)
Paul J. Cohen	SET THEORY AND THE CONTINUUM HYPOTHESIS
Walter Feit	CHARACTERS OF FINITE GROUPS
Marvin J. Greenberg	LECTURES ON ALGEBRAIC TOPOLOGY
Robin Hartshorne	FOUNDATIONS OF PROJECTIVE GEOMETRY
Irving Kaplansky	RINGS OF OPERATORS
Serge Lang	ALGEBRAIC FUNCTIONS
Serge Lang	RAPPORT SUR LA COHOMOLOGIE DES GROUPES
Ottmar Loos	SYMMETRIC SPACES: GENERAL THEORY
Ottmar Loos	SYMMETRIC SPACES: COMPACT SPACES AND CLASSIFICATION
I. G. Macdonald	ALGEBRAIC GEOMETRY: INTRODUCTION TO SCHEMES
George Mackey	INDUCED REPRESENTATIONS OF GROUPS AND QUANTUM MECHANICS
Richard Palais	FOUNDATIONS OF GLOBAL NON-LINEAR ANALYSIS
Donald Passman	PERMUTATION GROUPS
Jean-Pierre Serre	ABELIAN l-ADIC REPRESENTATIONS AND ELLIPTIC CURVES
Jean-Pierre Serre	ALGEBRES DE LIE SEMI-SIMPLES COMPLEXES
Jean-Pierre Serre	LIE ALGEBRAS AND LIE GROUPS
Shlomo Sternberg	CELESTIAL MECHANICS

SYMMETRIC SPACES

II: Compact Spaces and Classification

OTTMAR LOOS

University of Minnesota
and
Universität München

W. A. BENJAMIN, INC

New York 1969 Amsterdam

SYMMETRIC SPACES II: Compact Spaces and Classification

Library of Congress Catalog Card Number 69-18854
Manufactured in the United States of America
12345R32109

*The manuscript was put into production on August 8, 1968;
this volume was published on January 30, 1969.*

W. A. BENJAMIN, INC.
New York, New York 10016

PREFACE

This is the second volume of the lecture notes of a course on Topics in Advanced Differential Geometry given at the University of Minnesota during the academic year 1967-68. It is devoted mainly to the basic theory of compact symmetric spaces and their classification. Chapter V contains the structure theory of compact Lie groups and can be read independently from the rest of the book. Chapter V, §2 and Chapter VII, §1 can serve as a self-contained introduction to the theory of root systems. In Chapter VI, the corresponding theory for compact symmetric spaces is developed. The emphasis is on the root system of a symmetric space. Chapter VII gives the complete classification of compact symmetric spaces, including the determination of their root systems and multiplicities. The classical spaces (§2) are treated by relatively elementary methods and direct computations, while for the exceptional spaces (§3), a considerable machinery is required. The latter could have been applied to the classical spaces, too, resulting probably in a shorter exposition. The author felt, however, that an elementary and independent treatment of the classical spaces might be useful. In §4, the outer automorphisms of compact symmetric spaces are determined. Chapter VIII is expository in character, and is devoted to Hermitian symmetric spaces and their relations to Jordan algebras.

The notational conventions of Volume 1 are also used in this volume. For the convenience of the reader, we list some of them. If A and B are sets, then $A \setminus B$ denotes the set of all elements of A which are not in B, and $\bar{A}$ is the closure of a subset A of a topological space. The symbols $\mathbb{Z}, \mathbb{Z}_n, \mathbb{R}, \mathbb{C}, \mathbb{H}, \mathbb{O}$ denote the integers, the cyclic group of order n, the real numbers, the complex numbers, and the real division algebras of quaternions and Cayley numbers. $\mathbb{H}$ (resp. $\mathbb{O}$) have dimension 4 (resp. 8) over the reals. The complex conjugate, real part and imaginary part of a complex number x are $\bar{x}$, Re x, Im x. The connected component of the neutral element of a topological group G is denoted by G_0. If V is a real vector space, then V_C is the complexification of V.

CONTENTS

A Note from the Publisher

This volume was printed directly from a typescript prepared by the author, who takes full responsibility for its content and appearance. The Publisher has not performed his usual functions of reviewing, editing, typesetting, and proofreading the material prior to publication.

The Publisher fully endorses this informal and quick method of publishing lecture notes at a moderate price, and he wishes to thank the author for preparing the material for publication.

CHAPTER V

COMPACT LIE GROUPS

§1 MAXIMAL TORI

1. Notation and prerequisites

The reader is expected to be familiar with the basic theory of Lie groups as it can be found in Helgason [1], Chapter II, or in Hochschild [1]. We review some of the (mostly standard) notations used in the sequel. By G we will always denote a compact connected Lie group and by $\mathfrak{G}$ its Lie algebra. The exponential map from $\mathfrak{G}$ into G (which is surjective since G is compact) is denoted by $\exp$. If g is an element of G, then $\mathrm{Ad}g$ is the inner automorphism $a \to gag^{-1}$ of G and also the induced map (adjoint representation) on $\mathfrak{G}$. For $X,Y \in \mathfrak{G}$ we put $\mathrm{ad}X.Y = [X,Y]$. A torus is a compact connected abelian Lie group.

By T we will denote a maximal torus in G, by $\mathfrak{T}$ its Lie algebra. Then $\mathfrak{T}$ is maximal abelian in $\mathfrak{G}$. Indeed, if $\mathfrak{T}' \supset \mathfrak{T}$ is abelian, then $\overline{\exp \mathfrak{T}'}$ is a torus containing T. Conversely, if $\mathfrak{T}$ is maximal abelian, then clearly $T = \exp \mathfrak{T}$ is a maximal torus.

For a subset U of G, let $G^U = \{g \in G\colon ugu^{-1} = g$ for all $u \in U\}$ denote the centralizer of U in G. Similarly, we put $\mathfrak{G}^U = \{X \in \mathfrak{G}\colon \mathrm{Ad}u.X = X$ for all $u \in U\}$ and $\mathfrak{G}^V = \{X \in \mathfrak{G}\colon [Y,X] = 0$ for all $Y \in V \subset \mathfrak{G}\}$.

Besides the general theory of Lie groups, the following facts about compact Lie groups will be used without proof: There exists a positive definite $\mathrm{Ad}G$-invariant bilinear form $(\, , \,)$ on $\mathfrak{G}$. The Lie algebra $\mathfrak{G}$ is the direct product of an abelian Lie algebra and a compact Lie algebra (i.e., with negative definite Killing form). G is semisimple iff the center $Z(G)$ is finite iff the simply-connected covering group $\tilde{G}$ is compact. A torus has dense one-parameter subgroups and even dense subgroups generated by one element. The automorphism group of a torus is discrete. We will also use the fact that a complex finite-dimensional representation of a compact abelian group is the direct sum of one-dimensional representations. Proofs can be found for instance in Hochschild [1].

2. Maximal tori

THEOREM 1.1. a) *There exists* $X \in \mathfrak{T}$ *such that* $\mathfrak{T} = \mathfrak{G}^X$.

b) $\mathfrak{G} = \bigcup_{g \in G} \mathrm{Ad}g.\mathfrak{T}$; $G = \bigcup_{g \in G} gTg^{-1}$.

c) *Any two maximal tori are conjugate*.

d) *The center of* G *is the intersection of all maximal tori*.

Proof. a) Choose $X \in \mathfrak{T}$ such that the one-parameter group $\{\exp tX: t \in \mathbb{R}\}$ is dense in T . If $[X,Y] = 0$, then $\mathrm{Ad}\exp tX.Y = e^{\mathrm{ad}\,tX}Y = Y$. Hence $\mathrm{Ad}T.Y = Y$ and it follows $[\mathfrak{T},Y] = 0$. Therefore $\mathfrak{T} + \mathbb{R}Y$ is an abelian subalgebra containing $\mathfrak{T}$, and it follows $Y \in \mathfrak{T}$ by maximality of $\mathfrak{T}$.

b) Let X be as above, and $Y \in \mathfrak{G}$ arbitrary. The function

$$f(g) = (X , \mathrm{Ad}g.Y)$$

takes its minimum on the compact group G , say for $g = g_o$. Then we have

$$0 = \frac{d}{dt}\Big|_{t=0}(X, \mathrm{Ad}\exp tZ\mathrm{Ad}g_o.Y) = (X,[Z,\mathrm{Ad}g_o.Y]) = -([X,\mathrm{Ad}g_o.Y],Z)$$

for all $Z \in \mathfrak{G}$. It follows $[X,\mathrm{Ad}g_o.Y] = 0$ and by a), $\mathrm{Ad}g_o.Y \in \mathfrak{T}$. The second formula follows by applying exp , since the exponential map is surjective.

c) Let T' be another maximal torus, and X as in a).

Then there is $g \in G$ such that $\mathrm{Ad}g.X \in \mathfrak{T}'$. Hence $\mathrm{Ad}g^{-1}.\mathfrak{T}' \subset \mathfrak{T}$ which implies $\mathfrak{T}' \subset \mathrm{Ad}g.\mathfrak{T}$. By maximality, $\mathfrak{T}' = \mathrm{Ad}g.\mathfrak{T}$ and $T' = gTg^{-1}$.

d) This follows immediately from b) and c).

We define the <u>rank</u> of G to be the dimension of a maximal torus.

LEMMA 1.2. <u>Let</u> $S \subset G$ <u>be a torus and</u> $a \in G^S$. <u>Then there is a torus in</u> G <u>containing</u> a <u>and</u> S.

<u>Proof</u>. Let A be the closure of the subgroup generated by a and S. Then A_o is a torus containing S and $A = A_o \cup aA_o \cup \ldots \cup a^{m-1}A_o$ since A is compact. Hence $a^m \in A_o$ and $A/A_o \cong \mathbb{Z}_m$. Let b be an element in A_o whose powers are dense in A_o and choose $c \in A_o$ such that $(ac)^m = b$. Then the powers of ac are dense in A. Putting $ac = \exp Y$ where $Y \in \mathfrak{G}$, we see that the closure of the one-parameter group $\{\exp tY \colon t \in \mathbb{R}\}$ has the required properties.

COROLLARY. <u>The centralizer of a torus is connected. A maximal torus is its own centralizer and is a maximal abelian subgroup of</u> G.

Let now N be the normalizer of a maximal torus T.

Since the automorphism group of T is discrete, N_o centralizes T. Hence $N_o = T$ and $W = N/T$ is a finite group, called the <u>Weyl group</u>. W acts faithfully on T and (by the adjoint representation) on $\mathfrak{T}$.

LEMMA 1.3. <u>Let</u> $f: G \to H$ <u>be a surjective homomorphism. Then</u> $f(T)$ <u>is a maximal torus in</u> H.

<u>Proof</u>. Let $\mathfrak{K}$ be the Lie algebra of the kernel of f and $\mathfrak{H}'$ its orthogonal complement. Then $\mathfrak{G} = \mathfrak{K} \oplus \mathfrak{H}'$ is a direct sum of ideals, and f induces an isomorphism between $\mathfrak{H}'$ and $\mathfrak{H}$. We have $\mathfrak{T} = (\mathfrak{T} \cap \mathfrak{K}) \oplus (\mathfrak{T} \cap \mathfrak{H}')$. Indeed, let $X \in \mathfrak{T}$ be such that $\mathfrak{G}^X = \mathfrak{T}$ and let $X = X_1 + X_2$ be the decomposition relative to $\mathfrak{G} = \mathfrak{K} \oplus \mathfrak{H}'$. For an arbitrary $Y = Y_1 + Y_2 \in \mathfrak{T}$, we have

$$0 = [X,Y] = [X_1,Y_1] + [X_2,Y_2] ,$$

hence $[X_2,Y_2] = [X,Y_2] = 0$, i.e., $Y_2 \in \mathfrak{T}$.

This shows that $\mathfrak{T} \cap \mathfrak{H}'$ is maximal abelian in $\mathfrak{H}'$, hence $f(\mathfrak{T})$ is maximal abelian in $\mathfrak{H}$. It follows that $f(T)$ is a maximal torus in H.

3. <u>Root space decomposition</u>

As before, G is a compact connected Lie group and T

a maximal torus in G . Consider the adjoint representation of T on the complexification $\mathfrak{G}_C$ of $\mathfrak{G}$. By the complete reducibility of AdT on $\mathfrak{G}_C$ we have a decomposition

(1) $$\mathfrak{G}_C = (\mathfrak{G}_C)^T \oplus \Sigma \mathfrak{G}_\chi .$$

Here $(\mathfrak{G}_C)^T$ is the set of fixed points of AdT in $\mathfrak{G}_C$, the χ's are the different nontrivial characters of the representation, and

(2) $$\mathfrak{G}_\chi = \{Y \in \mathfrak{G}_C : \mathrm{Ad}x.Y = \chi(x)Y \text{ for all } x \in T\} .$$

We have $(\mathfrak{G}_C)^T = (\mathfrak{G}^T)_C = (\mathfrak{G}^{\mathfrak{T}})_C = \mathfrak{T}_C$ since $\mathfrak{T}$ is a maximal abelian subalgebra of $\mathfrak{G}$.

Every χ is a homomorphism from T into the circle group S^1 . We identify the Lie algebra of S^1 with $\mathbb{R}$. The exponential map is given by $\exp t = e^{2\pi\sqrt{-1}\,t}$. For any χ let $\alpha = \alpha_\chi$ be the induced map on the Lie algebras, so that we have

(3) $$\chi(\exp X) = e^{2\pi\sqrt{-1}\,\alpha(X)} , \quad X \in \mathfrak{T} .$$

Thus α is a linear form on $\mathfrak{T}$. The set R of linear forms obtained in this way is called the set of roots. Clearly the correspondence $\chi \to \alpha_\chi$ is one-to-one. Since none of the χ's is trivial, $0 \notin R$. The α's are also called angular parameters, since Ad exp X acts by rotation through an angle $2\pi\alpha(X)$ on $\mathfrak{G}_\chi$.

For an arbitrary linear form α on $\mathfrak{T}$, let

$$\mathfrak{G}^{\alpha} = \{Y \in \mathfrak{G}_C : [X,Y] = 2\pi\sqrt{-1}\,\alpha(X)Y \text{ for all } X \in \mathfrak{T}\} . \tag{4}$$

It follows then easily from (1), (2), and (3) that $\mathfrak{G}^0 = \mathfrak{T}_C$ and $\mathfrak{G}^{\alpha} = \mathfrak{G}_{\chi}$ if $\alpha = \alpha_{\chi} \in R$, and $\mathfrak{G}^{\alpha} = 0$ if $\alpha \neq 0$ does not belong to R. This together with the fact that any two maximal tori are conjugate shows that R is (up to isomorphism) uniquely determined by $\mathfrak{G}$. Also complex conjugation relative to the real form $\mathfrak{G}$ of $\mathfrak{G}_C$ gives $\overline{\mathfrak{G}^{\alpha}} = \mathfrak{G}^{-\alpha}$ since $\mathfrak{T}$ is real. Thus $\alpha \in R$ implies $-\alpha \in R$.

We collect our results in

PROPOSITION 1.4. <u>There is a direct sum decomposition</u>

$$\mathfrak{G}_C = \mathfrak{T}_C \oplus \sum_{\alpha \in R} \mathfrak{G}^{\alpha} \tag{5}$$

<u>where</u> $\mathfrak{G}^{\alpha}$ <u>is given by</u> (4) <u>and the set of roots</u> R <u>is a set of non-zero linear forms on</u> $\mathfrak{T}$. <u>We have</u> $\overline{\mathfrak{G}^{\alpha}} = \mathfrak{G}^{-\alpha}$ <u>and the negative of a root is again a root. For every root</u> α, (3) <u>defines a homomorphism</u> $\chi : T \to S^1$. <u>Denoting by</u>

$$U_{\alpha} = \{x = \exp X \in T : \chi(x) = e^{2\pi\sqrt{-1}\,\alpha(X)} = 1\}$$

<u>the kernel of</u> χ, <u>we have</u>

$$(\mathfrak{G}^x)_C = (\mathfrak{G}_C)^x = \mathfrak{T}_C \oplus \sum_{U_{\alpha} \ni x} \mathfrak{G}^{\alpha} \tag{6}$$

<u>for</u> $x \in T$.

LEMMA 1.5. Let rank $G = 1$ and $\dim G > 1$. Then $\dim G = 3$ and the Weyl group of G is $\mathbb{Z}_2$.

Proof. By Proposition 1.4, $\dim G = 2m+1$ is odd. $\mathrm{Ad}G$ acts on the unit sphere S^{2m} in $\mathfrak{G}$, and by Theorem 1.1, it acts transitively on the set of lines through the origin. It follows that the orbits of $\mathrm{Ad}G$ are open. Therefore $\mathrm{Ad}G$ acts transitively on S^{2m}. Let $T = \{\exp tX: t \in \mathbb{R}\}$ be a maximal torus. Then $\mathrm{Ad}g.X = X$ implies $gxg^{-1} = x$ for all $x \in T$, hence the isotropy group of X is T. Thus G/T is diffeomorphic with S^{2m}, and T is a circle. Part of the exact homotopy sequence is

$$\pi_2(S^{2m}) \to \mathbb{Z} \to \pi_1(G) \to 0 \tag{7}$$

since $\pi_1(T) = \mathbb{Z}$ and $\pi_1(S^{2m}) = 0$. It follows that T represents a generator of $\pi_1(G)$. Since G is transitive on S^{2m}, there exists $g \in G$ such that $\mathrm{Ad}g.X = -X$. If we connect g with e by a path, we obtain a homotopy between T and its "negative". Hence $\pi_1(G) = 0$ or $\pi_1(G) = \mathbb{Z}_2$. From (7) follows $\pi_2(S^{2m}) \neq 0$. Now $\pi_q(S^n) = 0$ for $q < n$ (see e.g., Spanier [1]). Hence $m = 1$ and $\dim G = 3$ (it is easily seen that $G \cong SO(3)$ or $G \cong S^3$).

Now the Weyl group is isomorphic with a subgroup of $\mathrm{Aut}\, S^1 \cong \mathbb{Z}_2$, and since there is $g \in G$ such that $\mathrm{Ad}g.X = -X$, it consists of two elements.

THEOREM 1.6. a) <u>The spaces</u> $\mathfrak{G}^\alpha$ <u>are one-dimensional. The only multiples of</u> α <u>which are roots are</u> $\pm\alpha$.

b) <u>The centralizer</u> G^{U_α} <u>of</u> U_α <u>in</u> G <u>is connected and</u>

$$(\mathfrak{G}^{U_\alpha})_C = \mathfrak{T}_C \oplus \mathfrak{G}^\alpha \oplus \mathfrak{G}^{-\alpha} .$$

c) <u>There exists exactly one involution</u> $s_\alpha \in W$ <u>leaving</u> U_α <u>pointwise fixed</u>.

<u>Proof</u>. a) Let $U = U_\alpha$ and $B = G^{U_o}$ the centralizer of U_o. By Corollary to Lemma 1.2, B is connected. Moreover, $T \subset B$ is a maximal torus in B. Let $K = B/U_o$. Then T/U_o is a maximal torus in K (Lemma 1.3) so that rank $K = 1$. Moreover, $\dim K > 1$ since $\mathfrak{B}_C \supset \mathfrak{T}_C \oplus \mathfrak{G}^\alpha \oplus \mathfrak{G}^{-\alpha}$ by (6). Now Lemma 1.5 shows $\dim K = 3$, hence $\dim B = \dim T + 2$. It follows that $\mathfrak{B}_C = \mathfrak{T}_C \oplus \mathfrak{G}^\alpha \oplus \mathfrak{G}^{-\alpha}$ and $\dim \mathfrak{G}^\alpha = 1$. If $c\alpha \in R$, then $(U_{c\alpha})_o = (U_\alpha)_o$. Hence $\mathfrak{T}_C \oplus \mathfrak{G}^\alpha \oplus \mathfrak{G}^{-\alpha} = \mathfrak{T}_C \oplus \mathfrak{G}^{c\alpha} \oplus \mathfrak{G}^{-c\alpha}$ and we must have $c = \pm 1$.

b) We have evidently $G^U \subset G^{U_o} = B$. On the other hand, $(\mathfrak{G}^U)_C = \mathfrak{T}_C \oplus \mathfrak{G}^\alpha \oplus \mathfrak{G}^{-\alpha} = \mathfrak{B}_C$ by (6). It follows that $G^U = B$ is connected.

c) Keeping the notations above, let $\pi\colon B \to K$ be the projection, let $S = T/U_o$ and let $N(S)$ resp. $N(T)$ be the normalizers of S resp. T. Then $\pi^{-1}(S) = T$ and $\pi^{-1}(N(S)) = N(T) \cap B$; hence Lemma 1.5 implies $\mathbb{Z}_2 \cong N(S)/S \cong (N(T) \cap B)/T$.

Let s_α be the involution in $W = N(T)/T$ corresponding to the nontrivial element in $\mathbb{Z}_2$. Then s_α acting on T is conjugation by an element of $B = G^U$ and leaves therefore U pointwise fixed. The unicity of s_α follows from the fact that it induces the orthogonal reflection in the hyperplane $\alpha = 0$ of $\mathfrak{T}$.

COROLLARY. U_α <u>has at most two components</u>.

<u>Proof</u>. $U_\alpha/(U_\alpha)_o$ is a finite and therefore cyclic subgroup of $T/(U_\alpha)_o = S^1$, and it is fixed under s_α. The automorphism of S^1 induced by s_α is the inversion, thus $U_\alpha/(U_\alpha)_o$ has at most two elements.

4. Inverse roots and the Weyl group

Recall that we let the Weyl group W act on T and $\mathfrak{T}$. The involution s_α corresponding to the root α (Theorem 1.6) leaves the hyperplane $\alpha = 0$ in $\mathfrak{T}$ pointwise fixed, since it is the Lie algebra of U_α. We denote by α^* the uniquely determined vector in $\mathfrak{T}$ such that

$$s_\alpha(\alpha^*) = -\alpha^* \quad \text{and} \quad \alpha(\alpha^*) = 2 . \tag{8}$$

α^* is called the <u>inverse root</u> of α. Then it follows immediately that

$$s_\alpha(X) = X - \alpha(X).\alpha^* \tag{9}$$

for all $X \in \mathfrak{T}$. Clearly, α^* is orthogonal to the hyperplane $\alpha = 0$ relative to $(\ ,\ )$, and if we define for any linear form λ on $\mathfrak{T}$ the vector $\vec{\lambda}$ by $(\vec{\lambda}, X) = \lambda(X)$ for all $X \in \mathfrak{T}$ we have

$$\alpha^* = \frac{2\vec{\alpha}}{(\vec{\alpha}, \vec{\alpha})} \tag{10}$$

Thus s_α is the orthogonal reflection in the hyperplane $\alpha = 0$. It should be noted that (10) is true for _any_ AdG-invariant scalar product on $\mathfrak{G}$, since α^* is defined independently of such scalar product.

We let now W also act on the dual of $\mathfrak{T}$ by

$$(w(\lambda))(X) = \lambda(w^{-1}(X)) . \tag{11}$$

If $w \in W$ is represented by an element n in the normalizer of T, one sees easily that $\mathrm{Ad}n.\mathfrak{G}^\alpha = \mathfrak{G}^{w(\alpha)}$. It follows that W permutes the roots.

PROPOSITION 1.7. _The map_ $\alpha \to \alpha^*$ _from_ R _into_ $\mathfrak{T}$ _has the following properties_.

a) $\alpha(\alpha^*) = 2$;

b) $\beta(\alpha^*) \in \mathbb{Z}$;

c) $\beta - \beta(\alpha^*).\alpha \in R$;

for all $\alpha, \beta \in R$.

Proof. a) was part of the definition.

b) Let $X \in \mathfrak{T}$ and $\alpha(X) = 1$. Then $\exp X \in U_\alpha$, thus by Theorem 1.6, $s_\alpha(\exp X) = \exp s_\alpha(X) = \exp(X - \alpha^*) = \exp X$, using (9). It follows that

$$\exp \alpha^* = e \tag{12}$$

and hence, since $e \in U_\beta$ for all $\beta \in R$, we have $e^{2\pi\sqrt{-1}\beta(\alpha^*)} = 1$, i.e., $\beta(\alpha^*) \in \mathbb{Z}$.

c) By (11) we have

$$(s_\alpha\beta)(X) = \beta(s_\alpha(X)) = \beta(X - \alpha(X)\alpha^*) = (\beta - \beta(\alpha^*)\alpha)(X) .$$

Since W leaves R invariant, the assertion follows.

If we introduce a scalar product in the dual of $\mathfrak{T}$ by $(\lambda,\mu) = (\vec{\lambda},\vec{\mu})$, then b) takes the more familiar form

$$\frac{2(\alpha,\beta)}{(\alpha,\alpha)} \in \mathbb{Z} .$$

We want to show next that W is generated by the s_α, $\alpha \in R$. To do this we need the concept of a Weyl chamber. It is defined to be a connected component of $\{X \in \mathfrak{T}\colon \alpha(X) \neq 0$ for all $\alpha \in R\}$. We remark that a Weyl chamber, being an intersection of finitely many half spaces, is an open convex cone.

THEOREM 1.8. The Weyl group acts simply transitively on the set of Weyl chambers and is generated by the reflections s_α $(\alpha \in R)$.

Proof. a) Let $\mathfrak{C}$ be a Weyl chamber, $w \in W$ and $w(\mathfrak{C}) = \mathfrak{C}$. Let X be an element of $\mathfrak{C}$ and $Y = \frac{1}{m}(X + w(X) + \ldots + w^{m-1}(X))$, where m is the order of w. Since $\mathfrak{C}$ is convex, Y belongs to $\mathfrak{C}$ and $w(Y) = Y$. For sufficiently small t, we have $0 < |\alpha(tY)| < 1$ for all $\alpha \in R$. Putting $y = \exp tY$, it follows from (6) that $\mathfrak{G}^y = \mathfrak{T}$. By Lemma 1.2, the centralizer of $\overline{\exp \mathbb{R}.Y}$ is T. If w is represented by an element n in the normalizer of T, we have

$$\exp tY = \exp tw(Y) = n(\exp tY)n^{-1}$$

which implies $n \in T$, and therefore $w = \mathrm{id}$.

b) Let $\mathfrak{C}$ and $\mathfrak{D}$ be Weyl chambers, and $X \in \mathfrak{C}$, $Y \in \mathfrak{D}$. If the segment from X to Y intersects a hyperplane $\alpha = 0$, then $\|X - Y\| > \|X - s_\alpha(Y)\|$.

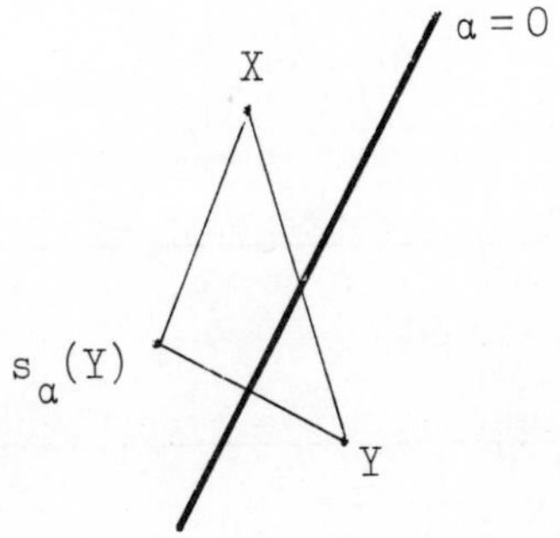

Let W' be the subgroup of W generated by all s_α. There exists $s \in W'$ such that $\|X - s(Y)\|$ is minimal. Then the segment $\overrightarrow{X\, s(Y)}$ cannot intersect any hyperplane $\alpha = 0$, hence $s(Y) \in \mathfrak{C}$. It follows that W' is transitive on the set of Weyl chambers. Now a) implies $W = W'$.

As a consequence we see that the Weyl group depends up to isomorphism only on $\mathfrak{G}$.

5. The diagram and the lattices

Let $\ell = \dim T$ be the rank of G . An element of G is called regular if the dimension of its normalizer is ℓ , it is called singular otherwise.

From Proposition 1.4, (6) follows that the set of singular elements in T is

(13) $$T_{sing} = \bigcup_{\alpha \in R} U_\alpha .$$

We also see that the center of G , which is contained in T , is given by

(14) $$Z(G) = \bigcap_{\alpha \in R} U_\alpha .$$

LEMMA 1.9. *The following statements are equivalent.*

a) G *is semisimple;*

b) *the intersection of the hyperplanes* $\alpha = 0$ $(\alpha \in R)$ *is zero;*

c) $R^* = \{\alpha^* : \alpha \in R\}$ *contains a basis of* $\mathfrak{T}$.

Proof. G is semisimple if and only if $Z(G)$ is finite. Therefore the equivalence of a) and b) follows from (14), since the Lie algebra of U_α is the hyperplane $\alpha = 0$. The equivalence of b) and c) follows from (10).

Assume now G to be semisimple. We make a number of definitions.

$$\mathfrak{T}_\alpha = \exp^{-1}(U_\alpha) = \{X \in \mathfrak{T}\colon\ \alpha(X) \in \mathbb{Z}\} .$$

$\mathfrak{T}_\alpha$ is a family of equidistant hyperplanes in $\mathfrak{T}$.

$D = \exp^{-1}(T_{sing}) = \bigcup_{\alpha \in R} \mathfrak{T}_\alpha$ (_diagram_)

$\Lambda_1 = \exp^{-1}(Z(G)) = \bigcap_{\alpha \in R} \mathfrak{T}_\alpha$ (_central lattice_)

$\Lambda(G) = \exp^{-1}(e)$ (_unit lattice_)

Λ_0 = the subgroup of $\mathfrak{T}$ generated by R^* (_fundamental lattice_).

A _lattice_ in $\mathfrak{T}$ is a discrete subgroup Λ such that $\mathfrak{T}/\Lambda$ is compact. Then we have

PROPOSITION 1.10. _Let_ G _be semisimple_.

a) Λ_0, $\Lambda(G)$ _and_ Λ_1 _are lattices in_ $\mathfrak{T}$ _such that_

$$\Lambda_0 \subset \Lambda(G) \subset \Lambda_1 .$$

Λ_0 _and_ Λ_1 _depend only on_ $\mathfrak{G}$, _and_ $Z = \Lambda_1/\Lambda_0$ _is a finite abelian group_.

b) $\Lambda_1/\Lambda(G) \cong Z(G)$.

c) _If_ $p\colon G' \to G$ _is a covering with kernel_ F, _then_

$$\Lambda_0 \subset \Lambda(G') \subset \Lambda(G) \ \ \text{and} \ \ F \cong \Lambda(G)/\Lambda(G') .$$

Proof. a) The first statement follows from Lemma 1.9. By (12), $\Lambda_0 \subset \Lambda(G)$ and obviously $\Lambda(G) \subset \Lambda_1$. Since Λ_0 and Λ_1 are defined in terms of R only, they depend only on $\mathfrak{G}$.

b) This follows from the fact that $\exp\colon \mathfrak{T} \to T$ is a homomorphism.

c) We identify the Lie algebras of G and G' by p. Then $T' = \exp_{G'} \mathfrak{T}$ is a maximal torus in G', and by a), $\Lambda_0 \subset \Lambda(G') \subset \Lambda(G)$. The kernel F is contained in $Z(G') \subset T'$, hence $\exp_{G'}^{-1}(F) = \exp_G^{-1}(e) = \Lambda(G)$ and it follows $F \cong \Lambda(G)/\Lambda(G')$.

This result shows that $\Lambda(\tilde{G})$, where $\tilde{G}$ is the simply connected group with Lie algebra $\mathfrak{G}$, realizes the "minimum" of all $\Lambda(G)$ and suggests that $\Lambda(\tilde{G}) = \Lambda_0$. We will prove in §3 that this is indeed the case. We can say however that <u>if</u> $\Lambda(G) = \Lambda_0$ for a group G, then G must be simply connected.

Example. Let $G = SU(n)$. Then

$$\mathfrak{G} = \{X = (x_{ik})\colon \operatorname{trace} X = 0 \quad \text{and} \quad \overline{x_{ik}} = -x_{ki}\}$$

and $\mathfrak{G}_C$ is the set of all complex $n \times n$ matrices of trace 0. Let T be the set of diagonal matrices in G:

$$T = \{t = \begin{pmatrix} t_1 & & 0 \\ & \ddots & \\ 0 & & t_n \end{pmatrix} \colon t_1 \ldots t_n = 1\}.$$

Clearly T is a torus of dimension $n-1$; and $\mathfrak{T}$ is the set of all purely imaginary diagonal matrices of trace 0. Let

E_{ik} be the matrix having 1 in the i-th row and k-th column, and zeros elsewhere. Then for $t \in T$:

$$\mathrm{Ad}t.E_{ik} = tE_{ik}t^{-1} = t_i t_k^{-1} E_{ik} \;, \quad (i \neq k) \;.$$

This shows that

$$\mathfrak{G}_C = \mathfrak{T}_C + \sum_{i \neq k} \mathbb{C}.E_{ik}$$

is the root space decomposition, and proves also that T is a maximal torus. The characters are $\chi_{ik}(t) = t_i t_k^{-1}$ and the roots are $\alpha_{ik}(X) = (x_i - x_k)/2\pi\sqrt{-1}$, where

$$X = \begin{pmatrix} x_1 & & 0 \\ & \ddots & \\ 0 & & x_n \end{pmatrix} \in \mathfrak{T} \;.$$

The bilinear form $(X,Y) = -\mathrm{trace}(XY)$ is positive definite and AdG-invariant. The Killing form is given by $\beta(X,Y) = 2n\,\mathrm{trace}(XY)$. Then we have

$$\vec{\alpha}_{ik} = \frac{1}{2\pi}\sqrt{-1}\,(E_{ii} - E_{kk})$$

$$\alpha^*_{ik} = 2\pi\sqrt{-1}\,(E_{ii} - E_{kk}) \;.$$

The unit lattice is $\Lambda = \{X \in \mathfrak{T} : x_i \in 2\pi\sqrt{-1}\,\mathbb{Z}\}$. Hence $\Lambda = \Lambda_0$ which shows in view of Proposition 1.10 c) that SU(n) is <u>simply connected</u>. The center of SU(n) consists of all multiples of the unit matrix, thus Z is isomorphic to the group $\mathbb{Z}_n$ of the n-th roots of unity.

Consider the special case $n=3$; let $\alpha = \alpha_{12}$, $\beta = \alpha_{23}$ and $\gamma = \alpha + \beta$. The roots are $R = \{\pm\alpha, \pm\beta, \pm\gamma\}$, the angle between α^* and β^* is 120°. As a basis for Λ_1, we can take $\frac{1}{3}(\alpha^* + \gamma^*)$ and $\frac{1}{3}(\beta^* + \gamma^*)$, and obtain the following picture.

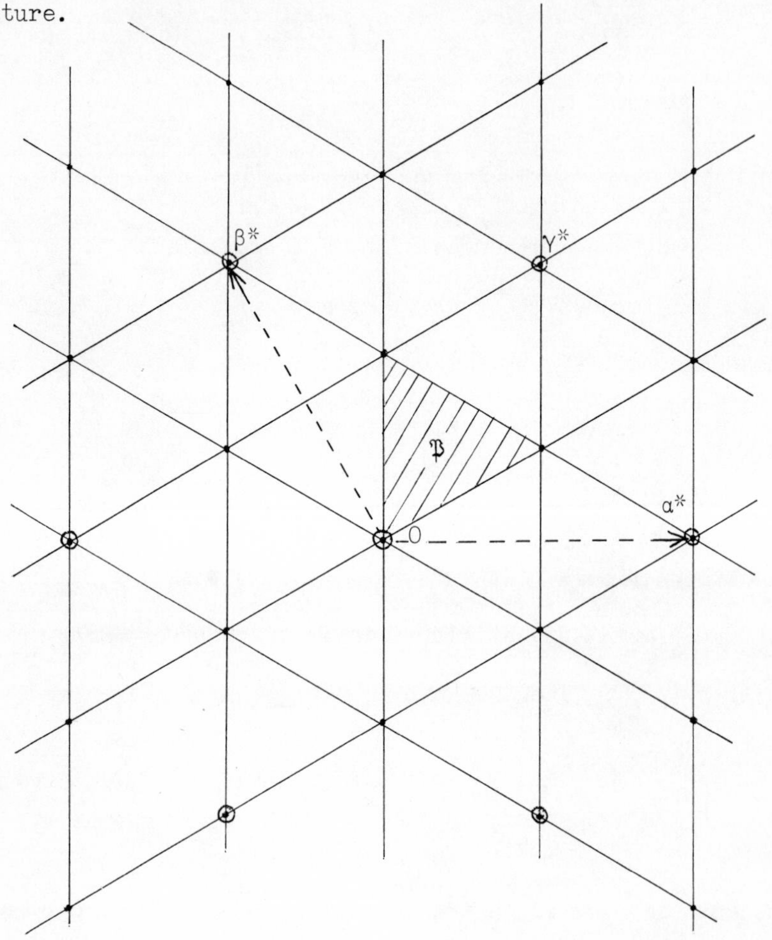

The points in Λ_1 are denoted by $\cdot$ and the points in Λ_0 by $\odot$.

§2 ROOT SYSTEMS

1. Basis of a root system

Motivated by §1, we make the following definition.

Let V be a vector space over $\mathbb{R}$, and V' its dual. A finite subset R of V' is called a root system for V if

(i) R generates V' as a vector space;

(ii) there is a map $*: R \to V$ such that

$$\alpha(\alpha^*) = 2$$

$$\beta(\alpha^*) \in \mathbb{Z}$$

$$\beta - \beta(\alpha^*).\alpha \in R$$

for all $\alpha, \beta \in R$.

A root system is called reduced if $\alpha \in R$ and $c\alpha \in R$ imply $c = \pm 1$.

The vector α^* is called the inverse of α. We put $R^* = \{\alpha^*: \alpha \in R\}$, called the inverse root system. If one lets $(\alpha^*)^* = \alpha$, one sees easily that R^* is a root system for V', since $(V')' = V$.

We see that the set of roots of a compact semisimple Lie group is a reduced root system. Non-reduced root systems occur in connection with symmetric spaces.

The rank of a root system is $\dim V$.

We denote by s_α the reflection in the root α, given by

$$s_\alpha(X) = X - \alpha(X).\alpha^* .$$

Thus s_α leaves the hyperplane $\alpha = 0$ pointwise fixed, and $s_\alpha(\alpha^*) = -\alpha$. If we let a linear transformation A of V act on V' by $(A(\lambda))(X) = \lambda(A^{-1}(X))$, we have

$$s_\alpha(\lambda) = \lambda - \lambda(\alpha^*).\alpha .$$

Hence we see that R is stable under the group W generated by all s_α, $\alpha \in R$, called the <u>Weyl group</u>. We denote by Aut R the group of all linear transformations of V (also acting on V') which leave R invariant. Since R is finite and generates V', Aut R is finite and W is normal in Aut R. The quotient group Aut R/W is denoted by E.

Choose now a positive definite scalar product on V which is invariant under Aut R. For $\lambda \in V'$ let $\vec{\lambda}$ be the vector in V such that $(\vec{\lambda}, X) = \lambda(X)$ for all $X \in V$. We introduce a scalar product in V' by $(\lambda, \mu) = (\vec{\lambda}, \vec{\mu})$. Then s_α is the orthogonal reflection in the hyperplane $\alpha = 0$. Therefore

$$s_\alpha(X) = X - 2\,\frac{(\vec{\alpha}, X)}{(\vec{\alpha}, \vec{\alpha})}\,\vec{\alpha} ,$$

and it follows

$$\alpha^* = \frac{2\vec{\alpha}}{(\vec{\alpha}, \vec{\alpha})} ; \quad \beta(\alpha^*) = \frac{2(\alpha, \beta)}{(\alpha, \alpha)} .$$

Let θ be the angle between two roots α and β. Then

$$\frac{2(\alpha,\beta)}{(\alpha,\alpha)} = 2\,\frac{\|\beta\|}{\|\alpha\|}\cos\theta$$

where $\|\alpha\|^2 = (\alpha,\alpha)$. Hence

$$\beta(\alpha^*).\alpha(\beta^*) = 4\cos^2\theta \in \mathbb{Z} .$$

It follows that $4\cos^2\theta$ can take the values 0, 1, 2, 3, 4 only; in the last case α and β are parallel. If we assume $\|\beta\| \geq \|\alpha\|$ and α not a multiple of β , we get the following list of possibilities for $\beta(\alpha^*)$.

$\alpha(\beta^*)$	$\beta(\alpha^*)$	θ	$\|\beta\|^2/\|\alpha\|^2$	$4\cos^2\theta$
0	0	$\pi/2$	-	0
1	1	$\pi/3$	1	1
-1	-1	$2\pi/3$	1	1
1	2	$\pi/4$	2	2
-1	-2	$3\pi/4$	2	2
1	3	$\pi/6$	3	3
-1	-3	$5\pi/6$	3	3

LEMMA 2.1. a) <u>Let</u> $\alpha,\beta \in R$ <u>be linearly independent. If</u> $\beta(\alpha^*) > 0$ <u>then</u> $\alpha - \beta \in R$.

b) <u>Let</u> $\alpha = c\beta$. <u>Then</u> $c = \pm\frac{1}{2}, \pm 1, \pm 2$.

<u>Proof</u>. a) The table shows that either $\beta(\alpha^*) = 1$ or $\alpha(\beta^*) = 1$. In the first case, $-s_\alpha(\beta) = -(\beta - \beta(\alpha^*)\alpha) = \alpha - \beta \in R$; in

the second, $s_\beta(\alpha) = \alpha - \beta \in R$.

b) Since $(c\alpha)^* = \frac{1}{c}\alpha^*$, it follows that $\beta(\alpha^*) = \frac{2}{c} \in \mathbb{Z}$ and $\alpha(\beta^*) = 2c \in \mathbb{Z}$.

As in §1, we define the <u>Weyl chambers</u> to be the connected components of

$$\{X \in V\colon \alpha(X) \neq 0 \text{ for all } \alpha \in R\} .$$

A <u>basis</u> (or a <u>simple root system</u>) of R is a subset B of R such that

(i) B is a vector space basis of V' ;

(ii) every $\beta \in R$ can be written as

$$\beta = \sum_{\alpha \in B} m_\alpha \alpha ,$$

where the m_α are integers of the same sign.

The elements of B are called <u>simple roots</u>.

THEOREM 2.2. <u>There is a one-to-one correspondence between bases and Weyl chambers. In particular, there exists a basis</u>.

<u>Proof</u>. Let B be a basis for R . Then clearly $\mathfrak{C} = \{X \in V\colon \alpha(X) > 0 \text{ for all } \alpha \in B\}$ is a Weyl chamber.

Conversely, let $\mathfrak{C}$ be a Weyl chamber, and R_+ the set of roots taking positive values on $\mathfrak{C}$. Clearly $R = R_+ \cup -(R_+)$. Let B be the set of all roots in R_+ which cannot be written as the sum of two other roots in R_+ . Then we show that B is a basis.

1° B <u>satisfies</u> (ii) .

<u>Proof</u>. It suffices to prove this for $\beta \in R_+$. Suppose β cannot be written as an integer linear combination with non-negative coefficients of elements in B . Choose an $X \in \mathfrak{C}$ arbitrary, and among all those β's the one for which $\beta(X)$ is minimal. Then $\beta \notin B$, hence $\beta = \gamma + \delta$ and $\gamma, \delta \in R_+$. It follows $\beta(X) = \gamma(X) + \delta(X)$ and $\gamma(X) < \beta(X)$, $\delta(X) < \beta(X)$. Hence γ and δ are integer linear combinations of elements of B , therefore β is such a combination; contradiction.

2° <u>If</u> $\alpha \neq \beta \in B$ <u>then</u> $(\alpha,\beta) \leq 0$ <u>and</u> $\alpha - \beta \notin R$.

<u>Proof</u>. If α and β are not linearly independent, we have $\alpha = 2\beta$ or $\beta = 2\alpha$ by Lemma 2.1 b), and both are impossible by the definition of B . Hence by Lemma 2.1 a), if $(\alpha,\beta) > 0$, we have $\beta(\alpha^*) > 0$ and $\alpha - \beta \in R$. If $\gamma = \alpha - \beta \in R_+$, it follows that $\alpha = \gamma + \beta$ is decomposable; if $-\gamma \in R_+$, $\beta = \alpha + (-\gamma)$ is decomposable. Hence $(\alpha,\beta) \leq 0$ and $\alpha - \beta \notin R$.

The theorem follows now from

LEMMA 2.3. <u>Let</u> B <u>be a set of linear forms on</u> V <u>such that</u> $(\alpha,\beta) \leq 0$ <u>and</u> $\alpha(X) > 0$ <u>for all</u> $\alpha, \beta \in B$ <u>and some</u> $X \in V$. <u>Then</u> B <u>is linearly independent</u>.

<u>Proof</u>. Assume that $\delta = \Sigma y_\beta \beta = \Sigma z_\gamma \gamma$, where $y_\beta, z_\gamma \geq 0$ and

β,γ run over disjoint subsets of B . Then $0 \leq (\delta,\delta) = \Sigma y_\beta z_\gamma (\beta,\gamma) \leq 0$ hence $\delta = 0$. It follows

$$0 = \delta(X) = \Sigma y_\beta \beta(X) = \Sigma z_\gamma \gamma(X) \ ;$$

this implies $y_\beta = z_\gamma = 0$.

Let R be a nonreduced root system, and put

$$R^{(1)} = \{\alpha \in R: \tfrac{\alpha}{2} \notin R\} \ ; \ \ R^{(2)} = \{\alpha \in R: 2\alpha \notin R\} \ .$$

Then $R = R^{(1)} \cup R^{(2)}$ and we have

PROPOSITION 2.4. $R^{(1)}$ _and_ $R^{(2)}$ _are reduced root systems._ _A basis_ $B^{(1)}$ _of_ $R^{(1)}$ _is also a basis for_ R , _and_ $B^{(2)} = \{m_\alpha \alpha: \alpha \in B^{(1)}$ and $m_\alpha = 2$ if $2\alpha \in R$, $m_\alpha = 1$ otherwise$\}$ _is a basis for_ $R^{(2)}$.

Proof. The only non-obvious statement is that $B^{(2)}$ is a basis for $R^{(2)}$. Clearly R , $R^{(1)}$ and $R^{(2)}$ determine the same Weyl chambers. Let $\mathfrak{C}$ be the Weyl chamber belonging to $B^{(1)} = \{\alpha_1,\ldots,\alpha_r\}$. Then (using the notation in the proof of Theorem 2.2) $B^{(2)} \subset R_+^{(2)}$. Let $\beta \in B^{(2)}$ and $\beta = \gamma + \delta$ with $\gamma,\delta \in R_+^{(2)}$. Then $\beta \notin B^{(1)}$ since $B^{(1)}$ is a basis for R . It follows that $\beta = 2\alpha_j$ for some $\alpha_j \in B^{(1)}$. If $\gamma = \Sigma m_i \alpha_i$, $\delta = \Sigma n_i \alpha_i$, we have $2\alpha_j = \Sigma(m_i + n_i)\alpha_i$ which implies $\gamma = \delta = \alpha_j \notin R^{(2)}$, contradiction.

COROLLARY. *Let* $\alpha \in R^{(1)}$. *Then there is a basis containing* α .

Proof. Choose $X \in V$ such that $0 < \alpha(X) < |\beta(X)|$ for all $\beta \neq \pm\alpha$. The basis determined by the Weyl chamber in which X lies contains α .

2. The diagram

Let R be a (not necessarily reduced) root system, and let

$$V_\alpha = \{X \in V: \alpha(X) \in \mathbb{Z}\}$$

for $\alpha \in R$. Thus V_α is a family of equispaced hyperplanes. We put

$$D = \bigcup_{\alpha \in R} V_\alpha ,$$

called the *diagram* of R . The connected components of $V \setminus D$ are convex polyhedra, called the *cells*.

Also let Λ_0 be the subgroup of V generated by the inverse root system R^* and let

$$\Lambda_1 = \bigcap_{\alpha \in R} V_\alpha = \{X \in V: \alpha(X) \in \mathbb{Z} \text{ for all } \alpha \in R\} .$$

Then Λ_1 is a lattice in V and from $\beta(\alpha^*) \in \mathbf{Z}$ for all $\alpha, \beta \in R$ we see that $\Lambda_0 \subset \Lambda_1$; also Λ_0 is a lattice. The finite abelian group

$$Z = \Lambda_1/\Lambda_0$$

is called the <u>center</u> of R .

The following group-theoretic Lemma is useful.

LEMMA 2.5. <u>Let</u> G <u>be a group acting on a set</u> S <u>and let</u> N <u>be a normal subgroup of</u> G <u>acting simply transitively on</u> S . <u>Then</u> G <u>is the semidirect product</u> $N \cdot H$ <u>where</u> H <u>is the isotropy subgroup of an element of</u> S <u>in</u> G .

<u>Proof</u>. Let $x \in S$. For every $g \in G$ there exists exactly one $n \in N$ such that $g(x) = n(x)$. Let $\varphi(g) = n^{-1}g$. Then φ is a homomorphism from G into G with kernel N and induces therefore a splitting $\bar{\varphi}\colon G/N \to G$. Clearly $\bar{\varphi}(G/N)$ is the isotropy group of x .

We let Λ_0 and Λ_1 act as groups of translations on V and denote by Γ the group generated by the reflections in the hyperplanes of the diagram.

PROPOSITION 2.6. a) Γ <u>is the semidirect product</u> $\Lambda_0 \cdot W$.

b) <u>For any</u> $w \in W$ <u>and</u> $X \in \Lambda_1$,

$$wX \equiv X \pmod{\Lambda_0} .$$

<u>Hence</u> $E = \mathrm{Aut}\, R/W$ <u>acts on</u> Z .

c) <u>The diagram is invariant under</u> $\Lambda_1 \cdot W$.

Proof. a) Clearly W leaves Λ_0 and Λ_1 invariant. Now a) follows from Lemma 2.5.

b) for $\alpha \in R$ and $X \in \Lambda_1$, we have

$$s_\alpha(X) = X - \alpha(X).\alpha^* \equiv X \pmod{\Lambda_0}.$$

Since W is generated by $s_\alpha(\alpha \in R)$, the assertion follows.

c) This follows immediately from the definitions.

For a description of the semidirect product $Z \cdot E$ see VII, Proposition 1.4.

Now let $\mathfrak{P}$ be a cell containing 0 in its closure $\bar{\mathfrak{P}}$. Then $\bar{\mathfrak{P}}$ is a convex compact polyhedron. Its faces determine hyperplanes, called the walls of $\mathfrak{P}$ (see p. 18).

PROPOSITION 2.7. a) Γ is generated by the reflections in the walls of $\mathfrak{P}$ and is transitive on the set of cells.

b) The Weyl group W is generated by the reflections s_α where α belongs to a basis of R, and W is transitive on the set of Weyl chambers.

Proof. a) Let Γ' be the subgroup of Γ generated by the reflections in the walls of $\mathfrak{P}$ and let $\mathfrak{Q}$ be another cell. Let $X \in \mathfrak{P}$ and $Y \in \mathfrak{Q}$. The orbit of Y under Γ' is discrete. This follows from $\Gamma' \subset \Gamma$ and the fact that $\Gamma = \Lambda_0 \cdot W$ is a discrete subgroup of the group of Euclidean motions of

V and hence acts properly discontinuously on V. Let $Z = v(Y)$ realize the minimum of the distances $\|X - w(Y)\|$, where $w \in \Gamma'$. We show that $Z \in \mathfrak{P}$ (compare the proof of Theorem 1.8). If $Z \notin \mathfrak{P}$, then the segment $\overrightarrow{XZ}$ intersects a wall of $\mathfrak{P}$. Hence by reflecting in this wall we would get $\|X - Z'\| < \|X - Z\|$.

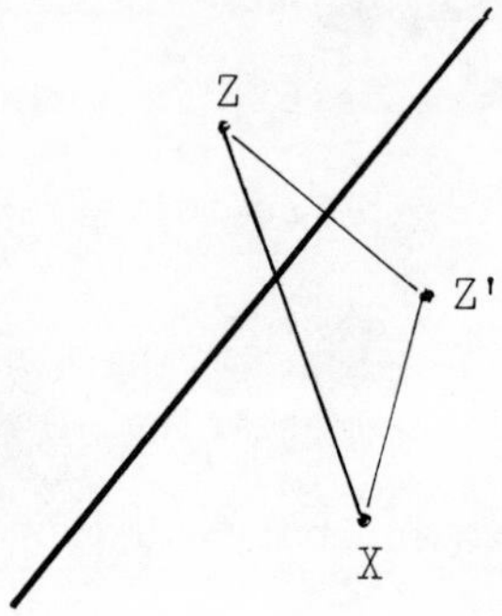

Thus $v(\mathfrak{Q}) = \mathfrak{P}$, since Γ' permutes the cells and Γ' is transitive.

Let s be the reflection in some hyperplane H of D. Then H bounds some cell $\mathfrak{Q}$, and there exists $w \in \Gamma'$ such that $w(\mathfrak{Q}) = \mathfrak{P}$. Let s' be the reflection in $w(H)$ which is a wall of $\mathfrak{P}$. Then $s = w^{-1}s'w \in \Gamma'$ and it follows $\Gamma = \Gamma'$.

b) The walls of a Weyl chamber $\mathfrak{C}$ are exactly the hyperplanes $\alpha = 0$ where α runs through the basis corresponding to $\mathfrak{C}$ (Theorem 2.2). The proof proceeds now analogously to a) and is left to the reader.

3. Simple transitivity of Γ on the cells

Let $H_1, \ldots, H_n$ be the walls of $\mathfrak{P}$, and let s_i be the reflection in H_i . For $w \in \Gamma$ let $\ell(w)$, called the <u>length</u> of w , be the smallest number r such that w can be written as a product of r reflections in the walls of $\mathfrak{P}$. A representation $w = s_{i_1} \ldots s_{i_r}$ is called <u>reduced</u> if $r = \ell(w)$. Then also $s_{i_k} \ldots s_{i_r}$ is a reduced representation $(1 \leq k \leq r)$, for if we could shorten it, then also the original one for w .

LEMMA 2.8. <u>The length of an element</u> w <u>in</u> Γ <u>is the number of hyperplanes of the diagram separating</u> $\mathfrak{P}$ <u>and</u> $w(\mathfrak{P})$.

<u>Proof</u>. 1° We start with the following observation: let H be a wall of $\mathfrak{P}$, let $w \in \Gamma$ and assume that $\mathfrak{P}$ and $w(\mathfrak{P})$ are on the same side of H . Then the hyperplanes of D separating $\mathfrak{P}$ and $sw(\mathfrak{P})$, where s is the reflection in H , are exactly the following:

1) the hyperplanes $s(H')$ where H' separates $\mathfrak{P}$ and $w(\mathfrak{P})$,

2) H itself.

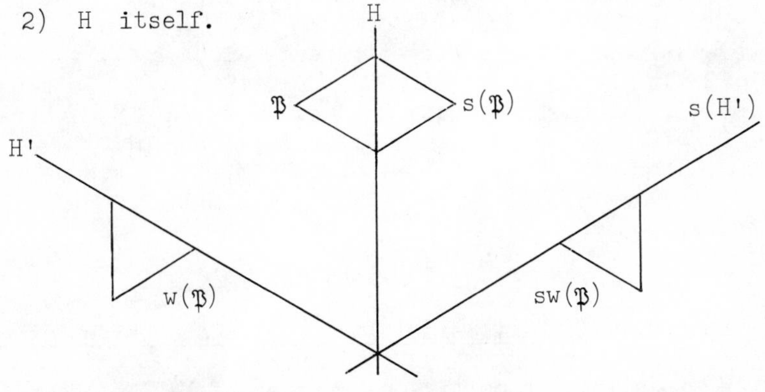

2° Let now $w = s_{i_1} \dots s_{i_r}$ be reduced. Then we prove by induction: the hyperplanes of D separating $\mathfrak{P}$ and $w(\mathfrak{P})$ are exactly $s_{i_1} \dots s_{i_{r-1}}(H_{i_r}), s_{i_1} \dots s_{i_{r-2}}(H_{i_{r-1}}), \dots, s_{i_1}(H_{i_2}), H_{i_1}$. These are all pairwise different.

The case $r = 1$ is clear. Let $w' = s_{i_2} \dots s_{i_r}$. Then $w = s_{i_1} w'$. We show that $\mathfrak{P}$ and $w'(\mathfrak{P})$ are not separated by H_{i_1}, then the first part of our assertion follows by 1°. Assume that H_{i_1} separates $\mathfrak{P}$ and $w'(\mathfrak{P})$. By induction hypothesis,

$$H_{i_1} = s_{i_2} \dots s_{i_m}(H_{i_{m+1}}) \text{ , for some } m \geq 1 \text{ .}$$

Hence

$$s_{i_1} = (s_{i_2} \dots s_{i_m}) s_{i_{m+1}} (s_{i_2} \dots s_{i_m})^{-1}$$

and therefore the representation

$$w = (s_{i_2} \dots s_{i_m} s_{i_{m+1}} s_{i_m} \dots s_{i_2}) s_{i_2} \dots s_{i_r} = s_{i_2} \dots s_{i_m} s_{i_{m+2}} \dots s_{i_r}$$

could be shortened, a contradiction.

By induction hypothesis, the hyperplanes $s_{i_2} \dots s_{i_{r-1}}(H_{i_r})$, $\dots, H_{i_2}$ are pairwise different; hence also $s_{i_1} \dots s_{i_{r-1}}(H_{i_r})$, $\dots, s_{i_1}(H_{i_2})$. Assume that $H_{i_1} = s_{i_1} \dots s_{i_m}(H_{i_{m+1}})$ where $m \geq 1$. Then $s_{i_1}(H_{i_1}) = H_{i_1} = s_{i_2} \dots s_{i_m}(H_{i_{m+1}})$, and we get a contradiction as above.

THEOREM 2.9. a) Γ <u>is simply transitive on the set of cells</u> <u>and</u> W <u>is simply transitive on the set of Weyl chambers</u>.

b) <u>Let</u> Λ <u>be a lattice such that</u> $\Lambda_0 \subset \Lambda \subset \Lambda_1$. <u>Then the subgroup</u> Ω <u>of</u> $\Lambda \cdot W$ <u>leaving</u> $\mathfrak{P}$ <u>fixed is isomorphic to</u> Λ/Λ_0 <u>and the order of</u> Ω <u>equals the number of points in</u> $\bar{\mathfrak{P}} \cap \Lambda$.

<u>Proof</u>. a) If $w \in \Gamma$ and $w(\mathfrak{P}) = \mathfrak{P}$ then the number of hyperplanes separating $\mathfrak{P}$ and $w(\mathfrak{P})$ is zero. Therefore $w = \mathrm{id}$ by Lemma 2.8. If $w \in W$ and w leaves a Weyl chamber $\mathfrak{C}$ invariant then also the unique cell which is contained in $\mathfrak{C}$ and contains the origin in its closure. Thus $w = \mathrm{id}$ and a) is proven.

b) By Proposition 2.6 b), W acts on Λ and Γ is normal in $\Lambda \cdot W$. It follows from Lemma 2.5 that $\Lambda \cdot W = \Gamma \cdot \Omega$ and hence

$$\Lambda/\Lambda_0 \cong \Lambda \cdot W/\Lambda_0 \cdot W = \Gamma \cdot \Omega/\Gamma \cong \Omega .$$

We define inverse maps $\Lambda \cap \bar{\mathfrak{P}} \to \Omega$ and $\Omega \to \Lambda \cap \bar{\mathfrak{P}}$ as follows. Let $Y \in \Lambda \cap \bar{\mathfrak{P}}$, then $\mathfrak{P} - Y$ is again a cell containing the origin in its closure. It follows that there exists a unique element $w \in W$ such that $\mathfrak{P} - Y = w(\mathfrak{P})$. Then the map $X \to w(X) + Y$ belongs to Ω . Conversely, if a transformation $\omega(X) = w(X) + Y$ belongs to Ω , we have $Y = \omega(0) \in \Lambda \cap \bar{\mathfrak{P}}$.

COROLLARY. $\mathrm{Aut}\, R \cong W \cdot E$.

Proof. This follows from a) and Lemma 2.5.

Let

$$\Lambda_2 = \bigcap_{\alpha \in R^{(2)}} V_\alpha .$$

Clearly Λ_2 is a lattice containing Λ_1 and $\Lambda_2 = \Lambda_1$ if R is reduced. Also let Aut D be the group of affine transformations of V leaving the diagram invariant.

PROPOSITION 2.10. Aut D is the semidirect product $\Lambda_2 \cdot \mathrm{Aut}\, R$.

Proof. Let $\psi: X \to \varphi(X) + Y$ belong to Aut D. An elementary geometric consideration shows that the vector which is normal to the family of hyperplanes V_α and of length twice the distance of two consecutive planes is just $2\vec{\alpha}/(\vec{\alpha},\vec{\alpha}) = \alpha^*$. It follows that φ preserves R^*, i.e., $\varphi \in \mathrm{Aut}\, R$. Now translation by Y preserves D, hence each V_α where $\alpha \in R^{(2)}$ (observe $V_{\alpha/2} \subset V_\alpha$). It follows that $Y \in \Lambda_2$.

§3 THE FUNDAMENTAL GROUP

We denote by G a compact connected semisimple Lie group, by T a maximal torus of G and by $\Lambda_0 \subset \Lambda(G) \subset \Lambda_1$ the lattices introduced in §1, 4. The purpose of this section is to prove that $\Lambda(G)/\Lambda_0$ is isomorphic to the fundamental group $\pi_1(G)$ of G. The proof requires some preparation.

1. Some facts from dimension theory

Let X be a metric space. We say that $\dim X \leq n$ if every open covering of X has a locally finite refinement such that the intersection of any $n+2$ of its members is empty. If $\dim X \leq n$ but not $\leq n-1$, we say that X has dimension n. The dimension thus defined is also called the Lebesgue covering dimension.

For the following facts quoted without proof, we refer to Nagata [1].

1° If X is a countable union of closed subsets each of which has dimension $\leq n$, then $\dim X \leq n$.

2° If A is a closed subset of X, then $\dim A \leq \dim X$.

3° The dimension of an n-simplex is n.

An immediate consequence is

4° An n-dimensional (in the usual sense) manifold has dimension n.

Let X be compact. The n-dimensional Hausdorff measure of X is defined by

$$\mu_n(X) = \sup_{\epsilon>0} \inf\{ \sum_{i=1}^{\infty} (\operatorname{diam} A_i)^n : X = \bigcup_{i=1}^{\infty} A_i \text{ , and } \operatorname{diam} A_i < \epsilon\} .$$

Here $\operatorname{diam} A = \sup_{x,y\in A} d(x,y)$ is the diameter of A in the metric d of X, and the A_i form a countable covering of X.

5° $\mu_{n+1}(X) = 0$ _implies_ $\dim X \leq n$.

6° _Let_ X _and_ Y _be compact differentiable manifolds and_ $\varphi\colon X \to Y$ _a differentiable map. Then_ $\dim \varphi(X) \leq \dim X$.

Proof. This follows from 5° and the fact that φ satisfies a Lipschitz condition

$$d(\varphi(x), \varphi(y)) \leq C.d(x,y)$$

for some constant C .

It is well known that 6° becomes false for an arbitrary continuous map.

7° _If_ $\dim X \leq n$, _then the Čech cohomology groups_ $\check{H}^q(X, \mathcal{S})$ _of_ X _with values in any presheaf_ $\mathcal{S}$ _of abelian groups vanish for_ $q > n$.

Proof. Let $\mathfrak{U} = (U_i)_{i \in I}$ be an open covering of X and let $C^q(\mathfrak{U}, \mathcal{S})$ be the q-cochains of $\mathfrak{U}$ with values in $\mathcal{S}$. An element in $C^q(\mathfrak{U}, \mathcal{S})$ is a map f assigning to each (q+1)-tuple $(i_o, \ldots, i_q) \in I^{q+1}$ an element $f(i_1, \ldots, i_q) \in \mathcal{S}(U_{i_o} \cap \ldots \cap U_{i_q})$. We set $f(i_o, \ldots, i_q) = 0$ for $U_{i_o} \cap \ldots \cap U_{i_q} = \emptyset$. The Čech group $\check{H}^q(X, \mathcal{S})$ is the inductive limit of the cohomology groups $H^q(\mathfrak{U}, \mathcal{S})$, $\mathfrak{U}$ running over all open coverings of X (see Godement [1] or Spanier [1] for basic facts about Čech cohomology).

A cochain f is called nondegenerate if $f(i_o,\dots,i_q) = 0$ in case two of the i_j's are equal. The nondegenerate cochains form a subcomplex $C^*_N(\mathfrak{U},\mathfrak{S})$ of the complex $C^*(\mathfrak{U},\mathfrak{S})$, and there is a projection $h: C^*(\mathfrak{U},\mathfrak{S}) \to C^*_N(\mathfrak{U},\mathfrak{S})$ commuting with the coboundary operator and homotopic to the identity (see MacLane [1], Chapter VIII, §6). It follows that $C^*(\mathfrak{U},\mathfrak{S})$ and $C^*_N(\mathfrak{U},\mathfrak{S})$ have the same cohomology, and by definition of dim X we see that every $\mathfrak{U}$ has a refinement $\mathfrak{U}'$ such that $C^q_N(\mathfrak{U}',\mathfrak{S}) = 0$ for $q > n$. It follows that $\check{H}^q(X,\mathfrak{S}) = 0$.

2. Regular and singular elements

LEMMA 3.1. The set of singular elements G_{sing} of G is compact and $\dim G_{sing} \leq \dim G - 3$.

Proof. By §1, (13), $T_{sing} = \bigcup_{\alpha \in R} U_\alpha$ is compact, and hence $G_{sing} = \varphi((G/T) \times T_{sing})$, where $\varphi(gT,x) = gxg^{-1}$, is compact. Now $\varphi((G/T) \times U_\alpha) = \varphi_\alpha((G/G^{U_\alpha}) \times U_\alpha)$ where $\varphi_\alpha(gG^{U_\alpha},x) = gxg^{-1}$. Thus by 4° and Theorem 1.6, we have $\dim(G/G^{U_\alpha}) \times U_\alpha = \dim G - (\dim T + 2) + \dim T - 1 = \dim G - 3$; hence the lemma follows from 1° and 6°.

Remark: It can be shown that actually $\dim G_{sing} = \dim G - 3$; see Helgason [1], Chapter VII, Theorem 4.7.

LEMMA 3.2. <u>The coset space</u> G/T <u>is simply connected</u>.

<u>Proof</u>. The simply connected covering group $p: \tilde{G} \to G$ is compact, and $\tilde{T} = \exp_{\tilde{G}}(\mathfrak{T})$ is a maximal torus in $\tilde{G}$. Moreover, the kernel of p is a subgroup of the center of $\tilde{G}$ and hence contained in $\tilde{T}$. It follows that $p^{-1}(T) = \tilde{T}$ and $\tilde{G}/\tilde{T}$ which is diffeomorphic with G/T is simply connected.

Let now $D = \exp^{-1}(T_{sing}) \subset \mathfrak{T}$ be the diagram, and let $\mathfrak{P}$ be a connected component (a cell) of $\mathfrak{T} \setminus D$ containing the origin in its closure. Let Ω be the subgroup of $\Lambda(G) \cdot W$ leaving $\mathfrak{P}$ invariant. Also denote by G_{reg} the set of regular elements in G.

PROPOSITION 3.3. <u>The simply connected covering space of</u> G_{reg} <u>is</u> $(G/T) \times \mathfrak{P}$ <u>under the map</u> $p(gT, X) = g(\exp X)g^{-1}$. <u>The fundamental group of</u> G_{reg} <u>is isomorphic to</u> Ω.

<u>Proof</u>. $\mathfrak{P}$ is a convex polyhedron; hence by Lemma 3.2, $(G/T) \times \mathfrak{P}$ is simply connected. Clearly $\exp \mathfrak{P} \subset T_{reg}$, therefore $p((G/T) \times \mathfrak{P}) \subset G_{reg}$. To prove the other inclusion, it suffices to show $p((G/T) \times \mathfrak{P}) \supset T_{reg}$, since p is equivariant relative to the action of G on the first factor of $(G/T) \times \mathfrak{P}$ and on itself by inner automorphisms, and since $G_{reg} = \bigcup_{g \in G} g\, T_{reg} g^{-1}$. Now $T_{reg} = \exp(\mathfrak{T} \setminus D)$ and $\Gamma = \Lambda_0 \cdot W$ is transitive on the set

of components of $\mathfrak{T}\setminus D$ (Proposition 2.7). Let $\mathfrak{Q} = w(\mathfrak{P}) + Y$ be another cell, $Y \in \Lambda_0$ and $w \in W$ be represented by an element n in the normalizer of T. Then, since $\Lambda_0 \subset \Lambda(G)$, we have

$$\exp \mathfrak{Q} = \exp w(\mathfrak{P}) = n(\exp \mathfrak{P})n^{-1} .$$

We show now that Ω acts freely on $(G/T) \times \mathfrak{P}$ on the right by $(gT,X).\omega = (gnT, w^{-1}(X - Y))$, where $\omega(X) = w(X) + Y$ and n represents w as above. Indeed, $(gT,X) = (gnT, w^{-1}(X - Y))$ implies $n \in T$; hence $w = \mathrm{id}$ and therefore $Y = 0$.

Finally, $p(gT,X) = p(g'T,X')$ implies $(g^{-1}g')\exp X'(g^{-1}g')^{-1} = \exp X$, and the connected component of the centralizers of $\exp X$ and $\exp X'$ is T. Hence $g^{-1}g' = n$ normalizes T. This implies $nX'n^{-1} - X = Y \in \Lambda(G)$, i.e., $X' = w^{-1}(X - Y)$, where $w = nT$, and the transformation $X \to w(X) + Y$ belongs to Ω. Conversely, it is easily seen that the action of Ω is compatible with p. This completes the proof.

COROLLARY. <u>Every element in</u> G <u>is conjugate to an element in</u> $\exp \overline{\mathfrak{P}}$, <u>thus</u> $\exp \overline{\mathfrak{P}}$ <u>is a fundamental domain for</u> G <u>acting on itself by inner automorphisms</u>.

<u>Proof</u>. Replace $\mathfrak{P}, \mathfrak{Q}, T_{reg}, G_{reg}$ by $\overline{\mathfrak{P}}, \overline{\mathfrak{Q}}, T, G$ in the

first part of the proof above. Since $\mathfrak{T}$ is the union of all $\bar{\mathfrak{Q}}$, it follows that $p((G/T)\times\bar{\mathfrak{P}})\supset T$. Hence $p((G/T)\times\bar{\mathfrak{P}})=G$.

3. Proof of the theorem

THEOREM 3.4. The fundamental group of G is isomorphic to $\Lambda(G)/\Lambda_0$. The order of the fundamental group equals the number of elements in $\bar{\mathfrak{P}}\cap\Lambda(G)$.

Proof. We consider homology and cohomology with integer coefficients. Part of the exact homology sequence is

$$H_2(G,G_{reg})\to H_1(G_{reg})\to H_1(G)\to H_1(G,G_{reg}) .$$

By duality (see Spanier [1], Chapter 6, Theorem 2.17, Corollary 8.8 and 8.9), we have $H_q(G,G_{reg})=\check{H}^{n-q}(G_{sing})=0$ for $q=1,2$, using 7° and Lemma 3.1. It follows $H_1(G_{reg})=H_1(G)$. Now $\pi_1(G)$ is abelian and $\pi_1(G_{reg})\cong\Omega\cong\Lambda(G)/\Lambda_0$ (Theorem 2.9 and Proposition 3.2) is also abelian. Hence $\pi_1(G)\cong H_1(G)\cong H_1(G_{reg})\cong\pi_1(G_{reg})\cong\Lambda(G)/\Lambda_0$.

COROLLARY. Let $\tilde{G}$ be the simply connected group with Lie algebra $\mathfrak{G}$, and $\bar{G}=\tilde{G}/Z(\tilde{G})$ the adjoint group. Then $\Lambda_0=\Lambda(\tilde{G})$ and $\Lambda_1=\Lambda(\bar{G})$, and we have $\Lambda_1/\Lambda_0\cong Z(\tilde{G})\cong\pi_1(\bar{G})$.

§4 CORRESPONDENCE BETWEEN ROOT SYSTEMS AND LIE GROUPS

1. Decomposition of root systems

Let R be a root system for the vector space V. Two roots α and β are said to be orthogonal if $\beta(\alpha^*) = 0$. In view of $\beta(\alpha^*) = 2(\alpha,\beta)/(\alpha,\alpha)$ with respect to some Aut R-invariant scalar product, this is equivalent with $(\alpha,\beta) = 0$. We say that a subset S of R is decomposable if it is the disjoint union of two nonempty orthogonal subsets, indecomposable otherwise. Suppose that $R = R_1 \cup R_2$ is decomposable and let V_i (resp. V_i') be the subspaces of V (resp. the dual V') spanned by R_i^* (resp. R_i). Then $V = V_1 \oplus V_2$ and the dual of V_i can be identified with V_i'. It follows easily that R_i is a root system for V_i $(i = 1,2)$. It is clear that every root system can be decomposed uniquely up to order into indecomposable root systems.

PROPOSITION 4.1. *Let* B *be a basis for* R. *Then* R *is decomposable if and only if* B *is decomposable*.

Proof. Clearly a decomposition of R gives a decomposition of B. Conversely, let $B = B_1 \cup B_2$. This gives an orthogonal decomposition $V' = V_1' \oplus V_2'$ into the subspaces spanned by B_1

and B_2 which is invariant under the Weyl group W, since W is generated by the reflections in the simple roots (Proposition 2.7 b)). Now every root is of the form $w(\alpha)$ or $2w(\alpha)$ for some $\alpha \in B$ and $w \in W$ (see Corollary of Proposition 2.4). Hence $R = (R \cap V_1') \cup (R \cap V_2')$ is a decomposition of R.

2. Complex semisimple Lie algebras

Let $\mathfrak{G}_C$ be a complex semisimple Lie algebra. A subalgebra $\mathfrak{H}$ of $\mathfrak{G}_C$ is called a Cartan subalgebra if $\mathfrak{H}$ is maximal abelian and ad $\mathfrak{H}$ acts completely reducibly on $\mathfrak{G}_C$. We give a review of the structure theory. For the proofs, we refer to Helgason [1], Jacobson [1], or Serre [1].

For a linear form α on a Cartan subalgebra $\mathfrak{H}$, let

$$\mathfrak{G}^\alpha = \{X \in \mathfrak{G}_C : [H,X] = \alpha(H)X \text{ for all } H \in \mathfrak{H}\} .$$

α is called a root if $\alpha \neq 0$ and $\mathfrak{G}^\alpha \neq 0$. Let R_C be the set of roots, and let $\mathfrak{H}_0$ be the biggest real subspace of $\mathfrak{H}$ where all roots take real values. Then we have

THEOREM 4.2. a) $\mathfrak{G}_C = \mathfrak{H} \oplus \sum_{\alpha \in R_C} \mathfrak{G}^\alpha$.

b) $\dim \mathfrak{G}^\alpha = 1$, *and* $[\mathfrak{G}^\alpha, \mathfrak{G}^\beta] = \mathfrak{G}^{\alpha+\beta}$ *if* α, β , *and* $\alpha + \beta \in R_C$.

c) R_C *is a reduced root system for* $\mathfrak{H}_0$.

d) <u>If</u> B_C <u>is a basis for</u> R_C , <u>then</u>

$$\mathfrak{H} \oplus \sum_{\alpha \in B_C} \mathfrak{G}^{\alpha} \oplus \mathfrak{G}^{-\alpha}$$

<u>generates</u> $\mathfrak{G}_C$.

THEOREM 4.3 (Unicity). <u>Let</u> $\mathfrak{G}_C$ <u>and</u> $\mathfrak{G}'_C$ <u>be semisimple Lie algebras with Cartan subalgebras</u> $\mathfrak{H}, \mathfrak{H}'$ <u>and root systems</u> R_C, R'_C . <u>Let</u> φ <u>be a</u> $\mathbb{R}$-<u>linear isomorphism between</u> $\mathfrak{H}_0$ <u>and</u> $\mathfrak{H}'_0$ <u>preserving the root systems. Then</u> φ <u>can be extended to an isomorphism between</u> $\mathfrak{G}_C$ <u>and</u> $\mathfrak{G}'_C$. <u>In particular</u>, $\mathfrak{G}_C$ <u>is uniquely determined</u> (up to isomorphism) <u>by</u> R_C .

(Existence) <u>For every reduced root system</u> R <u>there exists a complex semisimple Lie algebra with root system</u> R .

COROLLARY. <u>Under this correspondence, the decomposition of</u> R <u>into indecomposable components corresponds to the decomposition of</u> $\mathfrak{G}_C$ <u>into simple ideals</u>.

3. Applications to compact Lie groups

Let G be a compact semisimple Lie group, and T a maximal torus. Then it follows immediately from our results in §1 that $\mathfrak{H} = \mathfrak{T}_C$ is a Cartan subalgebra of $\mathfrak{G}_C$. Also $\mathfrak{H}_0 = \sqrt{-1}\,\mathfrak{T}$ and R_C is the set of linear forms on $\mathfrak{H}$ obtained by extending the linear forms $2\pi\sqrt{-1}\,\alpha$, where $\alpha \in R$, to $\mathfrak{T}_C$

in a $\mathbb{C}$-linear way. We write $R_C = 2\pi\sqrt{-1}\,R$ briefly.

THEOREM 4.4. a) (Unicity) <u>Let</u> G <u>and</u> G' <u>be compact semi-simple Lie groups with maximal tori</u> T <u>and</u> T' <u>and root systems</u> R <u>and</u> R'. <u>Let</u> φ <u>be a linear isomorphism between</u> $\mathfrak{T}$ <u>and</u> $\mathfrak{T}'$ <u>preserving the root systems and the unit lattices</u> $\Lambda(G)$ <u>and</u> $\Lambda(G')$. <u>Then</u> φ <u>can be extended to an isomorphism of</u> G <u>and</u> G'.

b) (Existence) <u>Let</u> R <u>be a reduced root system and</u> Λ <u>a lattice such that</u> $\Lambda_0 \subset \Lambda \subset \Lambda_1$. <u>Then there exists a compact semisimple Lie group with root system</u> R <u>and unit lattice</u> Λ.

<u>Proof</u>. a) By Theorem 4.3, there exists an isomorphism $\hat{\varphi}\colon \mathfrak{G}_C \to \mathfrak{G}'_C$ extending φ. If we choose as the scalar product $(\ ,\ )$ the negative of the Killing form of $\mathfrak{G}$ resp. $\mathfrak{G}'$, then φ preserves the scalar product. It follows that $\overrightarrow{\varphi(\alpha)} = \varphi(\vec{\alpha})$ for any $\alpha \in R$, where $\varphi(\alpha)$ is the linear form $\alpha \circ \varphi^{-1}$ on $\mathfrak{T}'$. Choose now a basis B of R and $E_\alpha \in \mathfrak{G}^\alpha$ such that $(E_\alpha, \bar{E}_\alpha) = 1$ for all $\alpha \in B$. We have $\bar{E}_\alpha \in \mathfrak{G}^{-\alpha}$, therefore $[X,[E_\alpha,\overline{E_\alpha}]] = 0$ for all $X \in \mathfrak{T}$. It follows that $[E_\alpha,\overline{E_\alpha}] \in \mathfrak{T}_C$ and from

$$(X,[E_\alpha,\overline{E_\alpha}]) = ([X,E_\alpha],\overline{E_\alpha}) = 2\pi\sqrt{-1}\,\alpha(X)$$

follows $[E_\alpha,\overline{E_\alpha}] = 2\pi\sqrt{-1}\,\vec{\alpha}$.

Let $B' = \varphi(B)$ and choose $E'_{\alpha'} \in \mathfrak{G}'^{\alpha'}$ for $\alpha' \in B'$ similarly. We then have for $\alpha' = \varphi(\alpha)$,

$$\hat{\varphi}(E_\alpha) = z_\alpha E'_{\alpha'} \quad (\alpha \in B)$$

since $\mathfrak{G}'^{\alpha'}$ is one-dimensional. There exists $H \in \mathfrak{T}_C$ such that $e^{2\pi\sqrt{-1}\,\alpha(H)} = 1/z_\alpha$ for all $\alpha \in B$. Let $\psi = \hat{\varphi} \circ e^{\mathrm{ad}H}$. Then ψ is an isomorphism extending φ, and we have for all $\alpha \in B$ that $\psi(E_\alpha) = E'_{\alpha'}$. It follows that

$$\psi([E_\alpha, \overline{E_\alpha}]) = [E'_{\alpha'}, \psi(\overline{E_\alpha})] = 2\pi\sqrt{-1}\,\overrightarrow{\alpha'} = [E'_{\alpha'}, \overline{E'_{\alpha'}}] .$$

On the other hand, $\psi(\overline{E_\alpha}) \in (\mathfrak{G}')^{-\alpha'}$ must be a multiple of $\overline{E'_{\alpha'}}$. Thus $\psi(\overline{E_\alpha}) = \overline{E'_{\alpha'}} = \overline{\psi(E_\alpha)}$ for all $\alpha \in B$.

We have shown that $\psi(\overline{Y}) = \overline{\psi(Y)}$ for all $Y \in \mathfrak{T}_C \oplus \sum_{\alpha\in B} \mathfrak{G}^\alpha \oplus \mathfrak{G}^{-\alpha}$. Since this is a set of generators of $\mathfrak{G}_C$ (Theorem 4.2), it follows that $\psi(\overline{X}) = \overline{\psi(X)}$ for all $X \in \mathfrak{G}_C$. This implies that $\psi(\mathfrak{G}) = \mathfrak{G}'$, i.e., ψ induces an isomorphism of the real forms $\mathfrak{G}$ and $\mathfrak{G}'$.

Now ψ can be extended to an isomorphism $\tilde{\psi}\colon \tilde{G} \to \tilde{G}'$ of the simply connected groups. Let $K = \exp_{\tilde{G}} \Lambda(G)$ and let K' be analogously defined. Then $\tilde{\psi}(K) = K'$ since φ preserves the unit lattices, and it follows that $\tilde{\psi}$ induces an isomorphism between $\tilde{G}/K = G$ and $\tilde{G}'/K' = G'$.

b) By Theorem 4.3 and IV, Theorem 2.2, there exists a compact Lie algebra $\mathfrak{G}$ with root system R. Let $\tilde{G}$ be the simply connected group with Lie algebra $\mathfrak{G}$. Then by Theorem

3.4, the group $G = \tilde{G}/\exp_{\tilde{G}}(\Lambda)$ has the required properties.

We remark that the condition $\varphi(R) = R'$ in Theorem 4.4 is equivalent with $\varphi(D) = D'$. Indeed, since R is reduced, the diagram determines the root system uniquely. Thus G is uniquely determined by the diagram and the unit lattice.

Let R and R' be root systems with lattices Λ and Λ' as in b). Then by a), (R,Λ) and (R',Λ') determine isomorphic groups if and only if there is an isomorphism $\varphi\colon R \to R'$ such that $\varphi(\Lambda) = \Lambda'$. In particular, the isomorphism classes of groups associated with a given root system R are in a one-to-one correspondence with the conjugacy classes of subgroups of $Z = \Lambda_1/\Lambda_0$ under $E = \mathrm{Aut}\, R/W$, since W acts trivially on Z (Proposition 2.6).

4. Automorphisms

Let G be as before and let $\mathrm{Aut}\, G$ (resp. $\mathrm{Int}\, G$) be the group of all (resp. the group of inner) automorphisms of G. By I, Theorem 4.8, $\mathrm{Aut}\, G$ is a Lie group, and by I, Theorem 4.9, $\mathrm{Int}\, G \cong G/Z(G)$ is the identity component of $\mathrm{Aut}\, G$.

THEOREM 4.5. a) An automorphism of G is inner if and only if it leaves a maximal torus pointwise fixed.

b) Aut G/Int G _is isomorphic to the subgroup_ E(G) _of_ E = Aut R/W _leaving the unit lattice_ $\Lambda(G)$ _invariant. In particular, if_ G _is simply connected_, Aut G/Int G $\cong$ E .

Proof. a) For $g \in G$ let Adg denote the inner automorphism determined by g , i.e.,

$$\mathrm{Ad}g.h = ghg^{-1} .$$

Since every element of G is contained in a maximal torus, it follows that an inner automorphism leaves some maximal torus pointwise fixed. Conversely, let $\varphi \in \mathrm{Aut}\, G$ and $\varphi(x) = x$ for all x in a maximal torus T . In the decomposition (5) of §1, we have then $\varphi(\mathfrak{G}^\alpha) = \mathfrak{G}^\alpha$ for all $\alpha \in R$. Let B be a basis of R , and choose $E_\alpha \in \mathfrak{G}^\alpha$ for all $\alpha \in B$. Then $\varphi(E_\alpha) = z_\alpha E_\alpha$ and $|z_\alpha| = 1$. Also $\varphi(\overline{E_\alpha}) = \overline{\varphi(E_\alpha)} = \overline{z_\alpha E_\alpha}$. It follows that $z_\alpha = e^{2\pi\sqrt{-1}t_\alpha}, t_\alpha \in \mathbb{R}$, and there exists a unique $X \in \mathfrak{T}$ such that $\alpha(X) = t_\alpha$ for all $\alpha \in B$, since B is a basis for the dual of $\mathfrak{T}$. Then we have

$$\mathrm{Ad}\exp X.E_\alpha = e^{2\pi\sqrt{-1}\,\alpha(X)}.E_\alpha = \varphi(E_\alpha)$$

for all $\alpha \in B \cup -B$ and also $\mathrm{Ad}\exp X.Y = Y = \varphi(Y)$ for all $Y \in \mathfrak{T}_C$. By Theorem 4.2 d), it follows that $\varphi = \mathrm{Ad}\exp X$ is inner.

b) Let $\varphi \in \mathrm{Aut}\, G$, and choose $g \in G$ such that $\varphi^{-1}(T) = gTg^{-1}$. Then $\varphi \circ \mathrm{Ad}g$ leaves T invariant and therefore induces an automorphism of R. Let $f(\varphi)$ be the class of this automorphism modulo W. Then $f(\varphi)$ is well defined: indeed, if also $\varphi^{-1}(T) = hTh^{-1}$, then $n = h^{-1}g$ normalizes T and $\varphi \circ \mathrm{Ad}g = \varphi \circ \mathrm{Ad}h \circ \mathrm{Ad}n$. Since n represents an element of the Weyl group, the assertion follows. Clearly, $f(\varphi)$ leaves the unit lattice invariant. One checks then easily that $f\colon \mathrm{Aut}\, G \to W$ is a homomorphism. If $\varphi = \mathrm{Ad}x$ is inner, then xg (with g as above) normalizes T and hence represents an element of W. Thus $f(\varphi) = e$. If conversely $f(\varphi) = \mathrm{id}$, then $(\varphi \circ \mathrm{Ad}g)|T = (\mathrm{Ad}n)|T$ for some n in the normalizer of T and hence $\varphi \circ \mathrm{Ad}g \circ \mathrm{Ad}n = \varphi \circ \mathrm{Ad}(gn)$ leaves T pointwise fixed. By a), φ is inner. Hence the kernel of f is $\mathrm{Int}\, G$. Conversely, by Theorem 4.4, a representative of $\eta \in E(G)$ can be extended to an automorphism φ of G and clearly $f(\varphi) = \eta$.

NOTES

§1 The exposition of the structure theory of compact Lie groups given here follows very closely the original papers by Stiefel [1] and Hopf [1].

§2 The definition of a root system adopted here is the one of Tits [1]. It has the advantage of being independent of a particular scalar product on the vector space V. The material in $\underline{\underline{1}}$ is mostly taken from Serre [1]. The significance of the diagram and the group Γ was emphasized by Stiefel. The proof of Theorem 2.9 is modelled after Iwahori-Matsumoto [1].

§3 Theorem 3.4 goes back to É. Cartan. As pointed out in Helgason [1], the inequality

$$\dim G_{sing} \leq \dim G - 3$$

does by itself not suffice to show that

$$\pi_1(G_{reg}) = \pi_1(G) .$$

However, since the homotopy groups in question are abelian (Proposition 3.3), one can deal with the homology groups instead, and there the difficulty mentioned above does not occur. The topology of the space G/T has been studied by Bott-Samelson [1]; Hopf and Samelson [1] proved that the Euler characteristic of G/T equals the order of the Weyl group.

§4 The basic facts on complex semisimple Lie algebras can be found in Jacobson [1] or Serre [1]. An elementary proof of the existence part of Theorem 4.3 has been given by Tits [1]. One can show that Aut G is isomorphic to the semidirect product of Int G and E(G) .

CHAPTER VI

COMPACT SYMMETRIC SPACES

§0 SUMMARY OF EARLIER RESULTS

In this section, we collect some of the results of Volume 1. References to Chapters I-IV which occur in the sequel can also be found here.

A <u>symmetric space</u> is a manifold M with a differentiable multiplication $\mu: M \times M \to M$, written as $\mu(x,y) = x \cdot y$, such that

(1) $x \cdot x = x$,

(2) $x \cdot (x \cdot y) = y$,

(3) $x \cdot (y \cdot z) = (x \cdot y) \cdot (x \cdot z)$,

(4) every x has a neighborhood U such that $x \cdot y = y$ implies $y = x$ for all y in U .

All symmetric spaces considered here are connected and have a base point, always denoted by o . The left multiplication with x is called the <u>symmetry around</u> x and denoted by S_x, i.e., $S_x(y) = x \cdot y$.

The group generated by all $S_x S_y (x, y \in M)$ is called the <u>group of displacements</u> and denoted by $G = G(M)$. It is a normal subgroup of the automorphism group Aut M and $\sigma: g \to S_o g S_o$ is an involutive automorphism of G. The <u>quadratic representation</u> $Q: M \to G$ is defined by $Q(x) = S_x S_o$. The group of displacements is a transitive Lie transformation group of M. If H denotes the isotropy group of o in G, then H lies between the group G^σ of fixed points of σ and its identity component. Also $M \cong G/H$ where the product in M is given by $aH \cdot bH = a\sigma(a)^{-1}\sigma(b)H$ (II, Theorem 3.1).

For every vector v in the tangent space $T_o(M)$, let $\tilde{v}$ be the vector field on M given by $\tilde{v}(x) = \frac{1}{2} v \cdot (o \cdot x)$. The set $\mathfrak{M}$ of these vector fields forms a Lie triple system, i.e., it is closed under the operation $[X,Y,Z] = [[X,Y],Z]$, and can be identified with $T_o(M)$ (II, Theorem 2.2). Putting $\mathfrak{H} = [\mathfrak{M},\mathfrak{M}]$, the Lie algebra $\mathfrak{G}$ of G is $\mathfrak{H} \oplus \mathfrak{M}$ and the Lie algebra of H is $\mathfrak{H}$. Also $[\mathfrak{H},\mathfrak{M}] \subset \mathfrak{M}$ and the adjoint representation of $\mathfrak{H}$ on $\mathfrak{M}$ is faithful (II, Theorem 3.1). We say that $\mathfrak{G}$ is the <u>standard imbedding</u> of $\mathfrak{M}$ (II, Proposition 2.3).

Every symmetric space has a canonical affine connection Γ such that the automorphisms are exactly the affine transformations (II, Proposition 2.5 and Theorem 2.6). Γ is torsion free and the curvature tensor, given at o by $R(X,Y)Z = -[X,Y,Z]$, has covariant derivative zero. The exponential map is denoted by Exp.

A Lie group L becomes a symmetric space, denoted by L^+, with the product $x \cdot y = xy^{-1}x$. The Lie triple system (= Lts) $\mathfrak{L}^+$ of L^+ is the Lie algebra $\mathfrak{L}$ of L as vector space, with the Lie triple product $[X,Y,Z] = \frac{1}{4}[[X,Y],Z]$ (II, §2, (5)). As an example, the quadratic representation Q is a homomorphism $M \to G^+$, inducing on $\mathfrak{M}$ the map $X \to 2X$.

The Lts of a symmetric space plays the same role as the Lie algebra of a Lie group. Thus the simply connected spaces are in a one-to-one correspondence with the Lts (II, Theorem 4.12), and there is a correspondence between sub-Lts and symmetric subspaces (III, Theorem 1.4). Also closed subspaces are submanifolds and therefore symmetric subspaces (III, Theorem 1.7).

Two elements x and y of a symmetric space M are said to <u>commute</u> if $x \cdot (a \cdot (y \cdot b)) = y \cdot (a \cdot (x \cdot b))$ for all $a,b \in M$. The <u>center</u> of M, denoted by $Z(M)$, is the set of all elements in M commuting with the base point o. Thus $Z(M) = \{x \in M\colon Q(x) \in Z(G)\} = \{x \in M\colon \mathrm{Ad} \circ Q(x) = \mathrm{id}\}$ is the "kernel" of $\mathrm{Ad} \circ Q$, where Ad is the adjoint representation of G on $\mathfrak{G}$. Also the tangent space $T_o(Z(M))$ of $Z(M)$ at o is the center of $\mathfrak{G}$ (III, Proposition 2.4). M is called abelian if any two elements commute. This is equivalent with the commutativity of G , and in this case $H = \{e\}$, i.e., $M = G^+$ (III, Proposition 2.5). The center has in a natural way the structure of an abelian Lie group, and acts freely on M . It is also pointwise fixed under H . The coverings $p: M \to M'$ are exactly the quotients of M by discrete subgroups of $Z(M)$ (IV, Theorem 4.2). If L is a Lie group considered as symmetric space $M = L^+$, then $Z(L) \subsetneq Z(M)$ in general; however, if $\mathfrak{L} = \mathfrak{C} \oplus [\mathfrak{L}, \mathfrak{L}]$ where $\mathfrak{C}$ is the center of $\mathfrak{L}$, then the centers coincide, and writing $M = G/H$, we have that H_o is the group of inner automorphisms of L (IV, Proposition 4.3).

A Lts $\mathfrak{M}$ is called semisimple if its standard imbedding $\mathfrak{G} = [\mathfrak{M}, \mathfrak{M}] \oplus \mathfrak{M}$ is a semisimple Lie algebra. Equivalent conditions are that $\mathfrak{M}$ is a direct sum of simple ideals or that the Ricci form $\rho(X,Y) = \mathrm{trace}(Z \to [Z,Y,X])$ is nondegenerate (IV, Proposition 1.3). The simple Lts are exactly those for which $\mathfrak{G}$ is either simple or the sum of two simple ideals. In the latter case $\mathfrak{M}$ is a simple Lie algebra considered as Lts (IV, Proposition 1.2). A symmetric space is called semisimple if its Lts is semisimple. In this case $Z(M)$ is discrete, G is the identity component of $\mathrm{Aut}\, M$, and $\mathrm{Aut}\, M$ is the group of isometries relative to the pseudo-Riemannian metric given by the Ricci tensor (IV, Proposition 1.4).

A symmetric space is called Riemannian if there exists a Riemannian metric invariant under all symmetries. It is called of compact (resp. noncompact) type if the Ricci tensor is negative (resp. positive) definite. A simply connected Riemannian space has a unique decomposition $M = M_o \times M_+ \times M_-$ where M_o is Euclidean, M_+ is of noncompact type, and M_- is of compact type (IV, Corollary 1 of Theorem 1.6). The spaces of noncompact type are diffeomorphic to Euclidean spaces and have trivial center (IV, Theorem 2.4).

The dual $\mathfrak{M}^*$ of a Lts $\mathfrak{M}$ has the same underlying vector space and the product $[X,Y,Z]^* = -[X,Y,Z]$. Duality interchanges the compact and noncompact type. A Lts of compact type is a Lie algebra considered as Lts if and only if the standard imbedding of its dual has a complex structure (IV, Theorem 1.9).

Every symmetric space is diffeomorphic to a vector bundle over a compact symmetric space (IV, Theorem 3.5). A consequence is that M is compact if and only if G is compact, and M is compact and semisimple if and only if M is of compact type if and only if the simply connected covering $\tilde{M}$ is compact (IV, Corollary of Theorem 3.5). The proof uses a decomposition theorem for Lie groups (IV, Theorem 3.2) which yields also the following result: for a connected Lie group L with an involutive automorphism σ, the group $L^\sigma/(L^\sigma)_o$ is finite and the direct product of cyclic groups of order two (IV, Theorem 3.4). The group G of displacements of a simply connected symmetric space is $\tilde{G}/Z(\tilde{G}) \cap \tilde{G}^\sigma$ where $\tilde{G}$ is the simply connected covering group of G (IV, Corollary of Theorem 3.4).

Let L be a connected Lie group and σ an involutive automorphism of L. Then $L_\sigma = \{x\sigma(x)^{-1}: x \in L\}$ is called the space of symmetric elements of L. It is a closed subspace of L^+ and $L/L^\sigma \cong L_\sigma$ under the map $q: xL^\sigma \to x\sigma(x)^{-1}$. Every symmetric space M can be realized as a space of symmetric elements L_σ, and in such a way that $Z(M) = Z(L) \cap M$ (IV, Theorem 4.6).

§1 MAXIMAL TORI

1. Notational conventions

In this chapter, M will always denote a compact connected symmetric space, G its group of displacements (which is compact by IV, Corollary of Theorem 3.5), and K the isotropy group of the base point o in G. We choose a positive definite AdG-invariant scalar product $(,)$ on $\mathfrak{G}$, which is also invariant under the automorphism σ induced by the symmetry S_o around the base point. Then, denoting as usual the Lie algebra of K by $\mathfrak{K}$ and the (-1)-eigenspace of σ by $\mathfrak{M}$, identified with the tangent space of M at o, we have the orthogonal decomposition $\mathfrak{G} = \mathfrak{K} \oplus \mathfrak{M}$. Also $\mathfrak{G}$ is the standard imbedding of $\mathfrak{M}$ (II, Proposition 2.3).

2. Maximal tori

A *torus* in M is a closed connected abelian subspace A containing the base point. By III, Proposition 2.5, A is actually a torus in the usual sense, and the product $x \cdot y$ is given by x^2y^{-1}, where xy is the Lie group multiplication in A. The unit element of A is the base point. Denoting by $\mathfrak{A} = T_o(A)$ the Lts of A, we have $(\mathrm{Exp}\, X)(\mathrm{Exp}\, Y) = \mathrm{Exp}(X+Y)$ for $X,Y \in \mathfrak{A}$. Also $0 = ([[X,Y],X],Y) = ([X,Y],[X,Y])$ implies that $\mathfrak{A}$ is an abelian subalgebra of $\mathfrak{G}$, and from $Q(\mathrm{Exp}\, X) = \exp 2X$ it follows that the quadratic representation $Q\colon M \to G$ induces a Lie group homomorphism $Q\colon A \to \exp \mathfrak{A}$. In particular, $Q(x)Q(y) = Q(y)Q(x)$ for $x,y \in A$.

LEMMA 1.1 *Let* $\mathfrak{A} \subset \mathfrak{M}$ *be an abelian subsystem. Then* $\mathrm{Exp}\, \mathfrak{A}$ *is a maximal torus if and only if* $\mathfrak{A}$ *is a maximal abelian subsystem.*

Proof. It suffices to remark that if $\mathfrak{A}' \supset \mathfrak{A}$ is abelian, then the closure of Exp $\mathfrak{A}'$ is a torus containing Exp $\mathfrak{A}$ (see III, Theorem 1.7).

In the sequel, A will denote a maximal torus in M and $\mathfrak{A}$ its Lts.

The following theorem is the exact analogue of V, Theorem 1.1 and, in fact, contains it as a special case, as we will point out later (see §3, 1).

THEOREM 1.2. a) There exists $X \in \mathfrak{A}$ such that $\mathfrak{A} = \{Y \in \mathfrak{M}: [X,Y] = 0\}$.

b) $\mathfrak{M} \bigcup_{k \in K_o} k.\mathfrak{A}$ and $M = \bigcup_{k \in K_o} k.A$.

c) Two maximal tori are conjugate by an element of K_o.

d) The center of M is the intersection of all maximal tori.

Proof. a) Choose $X \in \mathfrak{A}$ such that $\{\mathrm{Exp}\, tX: t \in \mathbb{R}\}$ is dense in A. If $[X,Y] = 0$, then $\mathrm{Ad}\exp tX.Y = e^{\mathrm{ad}\,tX}.Y = Y$, hence $[\mathfrak{A},Y] = 0$. Therefore $\mathfrak{A} + \mathbb{R}.Y$ is an abelian subsystem of $\mathfrak{M}$ containing $\mathfrak{A}$, and by Lemma 1.1, $Y \in \mathfrak{A}$.

b) Let X be as above, and $Y \in \mathfrak{M}$ arbitrary. The function

$$f(k) = (X, k.Y)$$

takes its minimum on the compact group K_o, say for $k = k_o$. Then we have

$$0 = \frac{d}{dt}\Big|_{t=0}(X, (\exp tZ)k_o.Y) = (X, [Z, k_o.Y]) = -([X, k_o.Y], Z)$$

for all $Z \in \mathfrak{K}$. Hence $[X, k_o.Y] = 0$, and by a), $k_o Y \in \mathfrak{A}$. The second formula follows by applying Exp, since for a compact Riemannian manifold the exponential map is surjective.

c) Let A' be another maximal torus, and X as in a). Then there is $k \in K_o$ such that $k.X \in \mathfrak{A}'$; hence $k^{-1}(\mathfrak{A}') \subset \mathfrak{A}$ which implies $\mathfrak{A}' \subset k(\mathfrak{A})$, and by maximality we have $\mathfrak{A}' = k(\mathfrak{A})$, $A' = k(A)$.

d) By IV, Theorem 4.2, the elements of $Z(M)$ are fixed under K . Hence it follows from b) and c) that $Z(M)$ is contained in the intersection D of all maximal tori. Now M is the union of its maximal tori. Therefore if $x \in D$, then $Q(x)$ commutes with $Q(M)$, which proves $x \in Z(M)$.

If we admit maximal tori in M which do not necessarily contain the base point o , we can express d) as follows: Two elements x and y of M commute (as defined in III, §2, 2) if and only if every maximal torus containing x also contains y .

The rank of M is the dimension of a maximal torus.

In case of a sphere, for example, the maximal tori are the great circles. Hence the rank is one. The intersection of all great circles containing a given point consists of this point and its antipodal point. Therefore the center is $\mathbb{Z}_2$.

The rank of any Riemannian symmetric space is defined as the dimension of a maximal abelian sub-Lts of its Lts. Clearly if M is of compact type and M^* is its noncompact dual, then M and M^* have the same rank.

3. Roots and multiplicities

We keep the preceding notations. If A is a maximal torus in M, then $Q(A)$ is a torus in G, and we consider its adjoint representation on the complexification $\mathfrak{G}_C$ of $\mathfrak{G}$. We get similarly to V, §1:

(1) $$\mathfrak{G}_C = (\mathfrak{G}_C)^A \oplus \Sigma\, \mathfrak{G}_\chi$$

where $(\mathfrak{G}_C)^A$ is the set of fixed points of $\mathrm{Ad}Q(A)$ on $\mathfrak{G}_C$ and the χ's are the different nontrivial characters of the representation with the corresponding eigenspaces

(2) $$\mathfrak{G}_\chi = \{Z \in \mathfrak{G}_C : \mathrm{Ad}Q(x).Z = \chi(x)Z \quad \text{for all} \quad x \in A\}.$$

Every χ determines a linear form $\lambda = \lambda_\chi$ on $\mathfrak{A}$ such that

(3) $$\chi(\mathrm{Exp}H) = e^{2\pi\sqrt{-1}\,\lambda(H)}, \quad H \in \mathfrak{A}.$$

The set R of linear forms on $\mathfrak{A}$ obtained in this way is called the set of <u>roots</u> of M relative to A.

For an arbitrary linear form λ on $\mathfrak{A}$ let

(4) $$\mathfrak{G}^\lambda = \{Z \in \mathfrak{G}_C : [H,Z] = \pi\sqrt{-1}\,\lambda(H)Z \quad \text{for all} \quad H \in \mathfrak{A}\}.$$

It follows then from (1), (2), (3), and $Q(\mathrm{Exp}H) = \exp 2H$ that $\mathfrak{G}^0 = (\mathfrak{G}^{\mathfrak{A}})_C$ and $\mathfrak{G}^\lambda = \mathfrak{G}_\chi$ if $\lambda = \lambda_\chi \in R$, and $\mathfrak{G}^\lambda = 0$ if $\lambda \neq 0$ does not belong to R. Here $\mathfrak{G}^{\mathfrak{A}} = \{X \in \mathfrak{G} : [X, \mathfrak{A}] = 0\}$ and since $Q(A) = \exp\mathfrak{A}$, we have $(\mathfrak{G}^{\mathfrak{A}})_C = (\mathfrak{G}_C)^{\mathfrak{A}} = (\mathfrak{G}_C)^A$. Moreover, since $\sigma|\mathfrak{A} = -\mathrm{id}$, we have $\mathfrak{G}^{\mathfrak{A}} = \mathfrak{K}^{\mathfrak{A}} \oplus \mathfrak{M}^{\mathfrak{A}}$ and since $\mathfrak{A}$ is maximal abelian in $\mathfrak{M}$, it follows

$$\mathfrak{G}^{\mathfrak{A}} = \mathfrak{K}^{\mathfrak{A}} \oplus \mathfrak{A} .$$

From (4) we also get by applying complex conjugation and σ that

$$\overline{\mathfrak{G}^{\lambda}} = \sigma(\mathfrak{G}^{\lambda}) = \mathfrak{G}^{-\lambda} .$$

Finally, since $\mathrm{Ad}Q(A)$ acts by automorphisms on $\mathfrak{G}_C$, we have $[\mathfrak{G}^{\lambda}, \mathfrak{G}^{\mu}] \subset \mathfrak{G}^{\lambda+\mu}$. Altogether we have

PROPOSITION 1.3. <u>There is a direct sum decomposition</u>

$$\mathfrak{G}_C = (\mathfrak{K}^{\mathfrak{A}})_C \oplus \mathfrak{A}_C \oplus \sum_{\lambda \in R} \mathfrak{G}^{\lambda} \tag{5}$$

<u>where</u> $\mathfrak{G}^{\lambda}$ <u>is defined by</u> (4) <u>and</u> R <u>is the set of nonzero linear forms</u> λ <u>on</u> $\mathfrak{A}$ <u>such that</u> $\mathfrak{G}^{\lambda} \neq 0$. <u>We have</u>

$$\overline{\mathfrak{G}_{\lambda}} = \sigma(\mathfrak{G}^{\lambda}) = \mathfrak{G}^{-\lambda} \tag{6}$$

<u>and</u>

$$[\mathfrak{G}^{\lambda}, \mathfrak{G}^{\mu}] \subset \mathfrak{G}^{\lambda+\mu} . \tag{7}$$

<u>For every root</u> λ , (3) <u>defines a homomorphism</u> χ <u>from</u> A <u>into</u> S^1 .

For every root $\lambda \in R$ we define the <u>multiplicity</u> $m(\lambda)$ to be the dimension (over $\mathbb{C}$) of $\mathfrak{G}^{\lambda}$. Also R is up to isomorphism uniquely determined by $\mathfrak{M}$, since $\mathfrak{G}$ (as the standard imbedding) is determined by $\mathfrak{M}$ and any two maximal tori are conjugate.

4. Real root space decomposition

PROPOSITION 1.4. *Let* $\mathfrak{K}_\lambda = \mathfrak{K} \cap (\mathfrak{G}^\lambda \oplus \mathfrak{G}^{-\lambda})$ *and* $\mathfrak{M}_\lambda = \mathfrak{M} \cap (\mathfrak{G}^\lambda \oplus \mathfrak{G}^{-\lambda})$.

a) *There are direct sum decompositions*

$$\mathfrak{K} = \mathfrak{K}^{\mathfrak{A}} \oplus \sum_{\lambda \in R_+} \mathfrak{K}_\lambda , \quad \mathfrak{M} = \mathfrak{A} \oplus \sum_{\lambda \in R_+} \mathfrak{M}_\lambda \tag{8}$$

where $R_+ \subset R$ *is a subset such that* $R = R_+ \cup (-R_+)$. *Moreover,*

$$m(\lambda) = \dim \mathfrak{K}_\lambda = \dim \mathfrak{M}_\lambda .$$

b) $\mathfrak{K}_\lambda = \{X \in \mathfrak{K}\colon [H,[H,X]] = -\pi^2\lambda(H)^2 X \text{ for all } H \in \mathfrak{A}\}$,

$\mathfrak{M}_\lambda = \{Y \in \mathfrak{M}\colon [Y,H,H] = -\pi^2\lambda(H)^2 Y \text{ for all } H \in \mathfrak{A}\}$.

c) $[\mathfrak{K}_\lambda, \mathfrak{K}_\mu] \subset \mathfrak{K}_{\lambda+\mu} + \mathfrak{K}_{\lambda-\mu}$

$[\mathfrak{K}_\lambda, \mathfrak{M}_\mu] \subset \mathfrak{M}_{\lambda+\mu} + \mathfrak{M}_{\lambda-\mu}$

$[\mathfrak{M}_\lambda, \mathfrak{M}_\mu] \subset \mathfrak{K}_{\lambda+\mu} + \mathfrak{K}_{\lambda-\mu}$

for $\lambda, \mu \in R \cup \{0\}$. *Here* $\mathfrak{K}_0 = \mathfrak{K}^{\mathfrak{A}}$ *and* $\mathfrak{M}_0 = \mathfrak{A}$.

d) *Let* $0 \neq X \in \mathfrak{K}_\lambda$ *and* $0 \neq Y \in \mathfrak{M}_\lambda$. *Then for* $0 \neq H \in \mathfrak{A}$, *we have* $\lambda(H) = 0$ *if and only if* $[H,X] = 0$ *if and only if* $[H,Y] = 0$.

Proof. a) From (6) follows that the subspace $\mathfrak{G}^\lambda \oplus \mathfrak{G}^{-\lambda}$ of $\mathfrak{G}_C$ is stable under conjugation and σ. Hence (8) follows from (5), since $\mathfrak{K}_\lambda = \mathfrak{K}_{-\lambda}$ and $\mathfrak{M}_\lambda = \mathfrak{M}_{-\lambda}$.

Consider the $\mathbb{R}$-linear map $Z \to \sigma(\overline{Z})$ of $\mathfrak{G}^\lambda$ into itself. It is involutive, and if $\mathfrak{G}^\lambda = \mathfrak{G}^\lambda_+ \oplus \mathfrak{G}^\lambda_-$ is the decomposition into the (± 1)-eigenspaces, we see that $\mathfrak{G}_-^\lambda = \sqrt{-1}\,\mathfrak{G}_+^\lambda$. Let $Z_i = X_i + \sqrt{-1}\,Y_i$, $i = 1,\ldots,m = m(\lambda)$, be an $\mathbb{R}$-basis of $\mathfrak{G}_+^\lambda$. Then this is a $\mathbb{C}$-basis of $\mathfrak{G}^\lambda$ and $X_i \in \mathfrak{K}$, $Y_i \in \mathfrak{M}$. It follows that $X_1,\ldots,X_m$, $Y_1,\ldots,Y_m$ is a $\mathbb{C}$-basis of $\mathfrak{G}^\lambda \oplus \mathfrak{G}^{-\lambda}$. Hence $X_1,\ldots,X_m$ is a basis of $\mathfrak{K}_\lambda$ and $Y_1,\ldots,Y_m$ is a basis of $\mathfrak{M}_\lambda$.

b) By (4) and the definition of $\mathfrak{K}_\lambda$, we clearly have $[H,[H,X]] = -\pi^2\lambda(H)^2 X$ for $X \in \mathfrak{K}_\lambda$ and $H \in \mathfrak{A}$. Conversely, let this be the case, and decompose $X = X_0 + \Sigma X_\mu$ as in (8). Then $[H,[H,X]] = -\pi^2 \Sigma\,\mu(H)^2 X_\mu = -\pi^2\lambda(H)^2 X$. It follows $X_0 = 0$ and $\lambda(H)^2 = \mu(H)^2$ for all μ such that $X_\mu \neq 0$. Therefore $X_\mu = 0$ for $\mu \neq \lambda$, since $\mathfrak{K}_{-\mu} = \mathfrak{K}_\mu$. Thus $X \in \mathfrak{K}_\lambda$. Similarly, one proves the second formula.

c) This is an immediate consequence of (7).

d) Let $[H,X] = 0$. Then $0 = [H,[H,X]] = -\pi^2\lambda(H)^2 X$ hence $\lambda(H) = 0$. Conversely, $\lambda(H) = 0$ implies $[H,[H,X]] = 0$ and hence $0 = (X,[H,[H,X]]) = -([H,X],[H,X])$ which shows $[H,X] = 0$. The proof of the second statement is similar.

As in the proof above, let $\mathfrak{G}_+^\lambda = \{Z \in \mathfrak{G}^\lambda : \sigma(\bar{Z}) = Z\}$. If $Z = X + \sqrt{-1}\,Y$, then $X \in \mathfrak{K}_\lambda$ and $Y \in \mathfrak{M}_\lambda$. We say that $X \in \mathfrak{K}_\lambda$ and $Y \in \mathfrak{M}_\lambda$ are <u>related</u> if $X + \sqrt{-1}\,Y \in \mathfrak{G}_+^\lambda$. By definition of $\mathfrak{G}^\lambda$, this is equivalent with

$$[H,X] = -\pi\lambda(H)Y \ ; \quad [H,Y] = \pi\lambda(H)X \tag{9}$$

for all $H \in \mathfrak{A}$.

For any linear form λ on $\mathfrak{A}$, we define the vector $\vec{\lambda}$ by $(\vec{\lambda},H) = \lambda(H)$ for all $H \in \mathfrak{A}$.

LEMMA 1.5. a) <u>For any</u> $X \in \mathfrak{K}_\lambda$ <u>there exists exactly one</u> $Y \in \mathfrak{M}_\lambda$ <u>which is related to</u> X. <u>The map</u> $X \to Y$ <u>is a linear isomorphism between</u> $\mathfrak{K}_\lambda$ <u>and</u> $\mathfrak{M}_\lambda$. <u>If</u> X <u>and</u> Y <u>are related, then</u>

$$[X,Y] = -\pi\vec{\lambda}(Y,Y) .$$

b) $[\mathfrak{K}_\lambda, \mathfrak{M}_\lambda] \subset \mathfrak{M}_{2\lambda} \oplus \mathbb{R}.\vec{\lambda}$.

c) <u>Let</u> X <u>and</u> Y <u>be related and let</u> $(\vec{\lambda},\vec{\lambda})(Y,Y) = 1$. <u>Then</u>

$$\mathrm{Ad}\exp tX.\vec{\lambda} = \vec{\lambda}\cos(\pi t) + \pi(\vec{\lambda},\vec{\lambda})Y\sin(\pi t) ,$$

$$\mathrm{Ad}\exp tY.\vec{\lambda} = \vec{\lambda}\cos(\pi t) - \pi(\vec{\lambda},\vec{\lambda})X\sin(\pi t) .$$

<u>Proof</u>. a) From (9) follows that Y is uniquely determined by X. Let $X = \frac{1}{2}(Z_+ + Z_-)$ where $Z_\pm \in \mathfrak{G}^{\pm\lambda}$. Then $\mathrm{Im}\, Z_+ + \mathrm{Im}\, Z_- = 0$ and $[H,X] = \pi\sqrt{-1}\,\lambda(H)\frac{1}{2}(Z_+ - Z_-) \in \mathfrak{M}_\lambda$. Hence $\mathrm{Re}\, Z_+ = \mathrm{Re}\, Z_- = X$, and if we put $Y = \mathrm{Im}\, Z_+$, we have $[H,X] = -\pi\lambda(H)Y$. Clearly $X \to Y$ is a linear isomorphism. Finally $(H,[X,Y]) = ([H,X],Y) = -\pi\lambda(H)(Y,Y)$, proving the asserted formula.

b) Let $Y \in \mathfrak{M}_\lambda$ and X the related vector in $\mathfrak{K}_\lambda$. Then

$$0 = ([H,H],X) = -\pi\lambda(H)(H,Y)$$

for all $H \in \mathfrak{A}$. Since $\mathfrak{A}$ contains a basis consisting of vectors such that $\lambda(H) \neq 0$, it follows that $\mathfrak{A}$ is orthogonal to $\mathfrak{M}_\lambda$. Let now $X_1 \in \mathfrak{K}_\lambda$ be arbitrary, and Y_1 related to X_1. Then by Proposition 1.4 c), we have $[X_1, Y] \in \mathfrak{A} \oplus \mathfrak{M}_{2\lambda}$. It follows

$$(H,[X_1,Y]) = ([H,X_1],Y) = -\pi\lambda(H)(Y_1,Y) ,$$

hence the component of $[X_1,Y]$ in $\mathfrak{A}$ is a multiple of $\vec{\lambda}$.

c) From (9) and a), we have $[X,\vec{\lambda}] = \pi(\vec{\lambda},\vec{\lambda})Y$ and $[X,[X,\vec{\lambda}]] = -\pi^2(\vec{\lambda},\vec{\lambda})(Y,Y)\vec{\lambda} = -\pi^2\vec{\lambda}$. Then we get

$$\operatorname{Ad}\exp tX.\vec{\lambda} = e^{\operatorname{ad} tX}.\vec{\lambda} = \sum_0^\infty \frac{t^{2n}}{(2n)!}(\operatorname{ad}X)^{2n}.\vec{\lambda} + \sum_0^\infty \frac{t^{2n+1}}{(2n+1)!}(\operatorname{ad}X)^{2n}[X,\vec{\lambda}]$$

$$= \vec{\lambda}\cos\pi t + \pi(\vec{\lambda},\vec{\lambda})Y\sin\pi t .$$

Similarly the second formula.

§2 WEYL GROUP AND SINGULAR ELEMENTS

1. The Weyl group

Let λ be a root, and χ, defined by §1, (3), the corresponding character. We put

$$U_\lambda = \text{kernel } \chi = \{x = \operatorname{Exp} H \in A : \chi(x) = e^{2\pi\sqrt{-1}\,\lambda(H)} = 1\} .$$

Since x belongs to the center of M if and only if $\operatorname{Ad}Q(x) = \mathrm{id}$ (see III, Proposition 2.4), it follows from §1, (1) and (2) that

(1) $$Z(M) = \bigcap_{\lambda \in R} U_\lambda .$$

For any subset U of M let

$$K^U = \{k \in K: k(x) = x \text{ for all } x \in U\} ,$$

$$\mathfrak{K}^U = \{X \in \mathfrak{K}: X(x) = 0 \text{ for all } x \in U\} ,$$

$$\mathfrak{M}^U = \{Y \in \mathfrak{M}: Y(x) = 0 \text{ for all } x \in U\} .$$

In the last two definitions, $\mathfrak{K}$ and $\mathfrak{M}$ are considered as sets of vector fields on M, see III, §3.

Finally, let

$$N(A) = \{k \in K: k(A) = A\}$$

be the normalizer of A in K and define the <u>Weyl group</u> of M by $W = N(A)/K^A$. Since the automorphism group of the torus A is discrete, we have $N(A)_o \subset K^A$ and W is finite. Also W acts faithfully on A and $\mathfrak{A}$.

PROPOSITION 2.1. a) *Let* $x \in A$. *Then*

$$\mathfrak{K}^x = \mathfrak{K}^{\mathfrak{A}} \oplus \sum_{U_\lambda \ni x} \mathfrak{K}_\lambda$$

and $\mathfrak{M}^x = \Sigma\, \mathfrak{M}_\lambda$, *where the sum is taken over all* λ *such that* $x^2 \in U_\lambda$ *but* $x \notin U_\lambda$.

b) $Z(M) = \{x \in M: k(x) = x \text{ for all } k \in K_o\}$.

c) *For every root* λ *there exists exactly one involution* $s_\lambda \in W$ *leaving* U_λ *pointwise fixed*.

<u>Proof</u>. a) Let $x = \operatorname{Exp} H$ and $X \in \mathfrak{K}$. Then $X(x) = 0$ if and only if $\exp tX.x = (\exp tX \exp H)K = (\exp H)K$ for all t if and only if $(\exp H)^{-1}\exp tX \exp H \in K$ for all t if and only if $e^{-\operatorname{ad}H}.X \in \mathfrak{K}$. Now decompose $X = X_o + \Sigma X_\lambda$ according to §1, (8). If we denote by Y_λ the vector in $\mathfrak{M}_\lambda$ related to X_λ, we have by §1, (9)

$$e^{-\operatorname{ad}H}.X_\lambda = X_\lambda \cos(\pi\lambda(H)) + Y_\lambda \sin(\pi\lambda(H)) . \tag{2}$$

Hence $e^{-\operatorname{ad}H}.X \in \mathfrak{K}$ iff $\sin(\pi\lambda(H)) = 0$ whenever $Y_\lambda \neq 0$ iff $x = \operatorname{Exp} H \in U_\lambda$ whenever $X_\lambda \neq 0$. This proves the first formula.

Similarly, $Y(x) = 0$ if and only if $e^{-\operatorname{ad}H}.Y \in \mathfrak{K}$, and for $Y = Y_o + \Sigma Y_\lambda$ we have

$$e^{-\operatorname{ad}H}Y_\lambda = -X_\lambda \sin(\pi\lambda(H)) + Y_\lambda \cos(\pi\lambda(H)) .$$

The assertion follows since $x^2 = \operatorname{Exp} 2H$.

b) This follows from (1) and a).

c) Choose X and Y as in Lemma 1.5 c). Then

$$\operatorname{Ad} \exp X.\vec{\lambda} = -\vec{\lambda} ,$$

and $\operatorname{Ad}\exp X.H = H$ for all H such that $\lambda(H) = 0$ by Proposition 1.4 d). It follows that $\exp X = n \in N(A)$ represents an involutive element $s_\lambda \in W$, since it induces the orthogonal reflection in the hyperplane $\lambda = 0$ of $\mathfrak{A}$ (observe that $\vec{\lambda}$ is orthogonal to this hyperplane). Now let $x = \operatorname{Exp} H \in U_\lambda$. Then $\lambda(H) \in \mathbb{Z}$, hence $e^{-\operatorname{ad}H}.X = \pm X$ by (2). This implies $\exp X \exp H = \exp H \exp \pm X$ and hence $nx = x$. The unicity of

s_λ follows from the fact that every involution in W leaving U_λ pointwise fixed must induce the orthogonal reflection in the hyperplane $\lambda = 0$ in $\mathfrak{A}$.

COROLLARY. U_λ <u>has at most two components. If</u> λ <u>and</u> 2λ <u>belong to</u> R , <u>then</u> $U_\lambda = (U_{2\lambda})_o$ <u>and</u> $U_{2\lambda}$ <u>has two components</u>.

<u>Proof</u>. The first statement follows as in V, Corollary of Theorem 1.6. Clearly $U_\lambda \subset U_{2\lambda}$ and $U_\lambda \neq U_{2\lambda}$. Since they have the same Lie algebra, namely the hyperplane $\lambda = 0$, the assertion follows.

We can now prove a number of results which are exactly analogous to those of V, §1, <u>4</u>. For any root λ let the <u>inverse root</u> λ^* be the unique vector in $\mathfrak{A}$ such that

(3) $$\lambda(\lambda^*) = 2 \; ; \quad s_\lambda(\lambda^*) = -\lambda^* \; .$$

As in Chapter V, one sees that

$$\lambda^* = \frac{2\vec{\lambda}}{(\vec{\lambda},\vec{\lambda})} \; ,$$

which is true for any choice of (,) . Also W acting on the dual of $\mathfrak{A}$ (see V, §1, (11)) leaves R invariant. We have

(4) $$\mu(\lambda^*) \in \mathbf{Z} \; ; \quad \mu - \mu(\lambda^*)\lambda \in R$$

for all $\lambda, \mu \in R$. The proof of (4) is verbatim the same as that of V, Proposition 1.7, replacing exp by Exp and $\mathfrak{T}$ by $\mathfrak{A}$. In particular,

$$\operatorname{Exp} \lambda^* = o \tag{5}$$

for all $\lambda \in R$.

Finally, we define the Weyl chambers as in V, §1, 4 and have

PROPOSITION 2.2. <u>The Weyl group acts simply transitively on the set of Weyl chambers and is generated by the reflections</u> $s_\lambda (\lambda \in R)$.

<u>Proof</u>. It suffices to give a proof of part a) of the proof of V, Theorem 1.8; part b) remains unchanged. Thus assume that $w(\mathfrak{C}) = \mathfrak{C}$ for $w \in W$ and a Weyl chamber $\mathfrak{C}$. As before, we find $Y \in \mathfrak{C}$ such that $w(Y) = Y$. Let $k \in N(A)$ be a representative of w. Then k belongs to the centralizer of the torus $\overline{\exp \mathbb{R}Y}$ in G, which is connected (V, Corollary of Lemma 1.2). This centralizer has Lie algebra $\mathfrak{G}^Y = \mathfrak{G}^{\mathfrak{A}}$, which follows from $\lambda(Y) \neq 0$ for all $\lambda \in R$ and (5) in Proposition 1.3. Therefore, $k = \exp X$ for some $X \in \mathfrak{G}^{\mathfrak{A}}$ and hence k acts trivially on $\mathfrak{A}$, and $w = \mathrm{id}$.

As a consequence, we see that $W \cong (N(A) \cap K_o)/(K_o)^A$, since the proof of Proposition 1.6 shows that every s_λ can be represented by an element in K_o. Also, W depends only on $\mathfrak{M}$ and $\mathfrak{A}$.

2. Regular and singular elements

LEMMA 2.3. The following statements are equivalent.

a) M is semisimple;

b) Z(M) is finite;

c) the intersection of the hyperplanes $\lambda = 0$, $(\lambda \in R)$ is zero;

d) R* contains a basis of $\mathfrak{A}$.

Proof. The equivalence of b), c), and d) follows as in V, Lemma 1.9, since $Z(M) = \bigcap_{\lambda \in R} U_\lambda$. By IV, Proposition 1.4, a semisimple symmetric space has discrete center, and since M is compact Z(M) is finite. Conversely, if Z(M) is finite, the center of $\mathfrak{G}$ is trivial by III, Proposition 2.4, and since $\mathfrak{G}$ is the Lie algebra of a compact Lie group, $\mathfrak{G}$ is semisimple. Hence M is semisimple.

An element $x \in M$ is called regular resp. singular if $\dim \mathfrak{K}^x = \dim \mathfrak{K}^{\mathfrak{A}}$ resp. $\dim \mathfrak{K}^x > \dim \mathfrak{K}^{\mathfrak{A}}$. From Proposition 1.6 follows that the set of singular elements in A is

(6) $$A_{sing} = \bigcup_{\lambda \in R} U_\lambda .$$

PROPOSITION 2.4. Let M be semisimple; then

a) R is a root system for $\mathfrak{A}$. The Weyl group of R (as defined in V, §2) _is isomorphic to_ $N(A)/K^A$.

b) _Let_

$$\Lambda(M) = \{H \in \mathfrak{A}: \text{ Exp } H = o\}$$

and let Λ_0 , Λ_1 _and_ D _be defined as in_ V, §2, 2. _Then_ $\Lambda_0 \subset \Lambda(M) \subset \Lambda_1$ _and_ $D = \text{Exp}^{-1}(A_{sing})$ _and_ $\Lambda_1 = \text{Exp}^{-1}(Z(M))$. _Also_ $Z(M) \cong \Lambda_1/\Lambda(M)$.

c) _If_ $p: M' \to M$ _is a covering with fibre_ $F = p^{-1}(p(o))$, _then_ $\Lambda_0 \subset \Lambda(M') \subset \Lambda(M)$ _and_ $F \cong \Lambda(M)/\Lambda(M')$.

Proof. a) Follows from (3), (4), Proposition 2.2 and Lemma 2.3.

b) Since $\text{Exp}^{-1}(U_\lambda) = \mathfrak{A}_\lambda = \{H \in \mathfrak{A}: \lambda(H) \in \mathbb{Z}\}$, this is an immediate consequence of (1), (5), (6), and the definitions.

c) The proof is analogous to V, Proposition 1.10, using IV, Theorem 4.2.

Again $\pi_1(M) = \Lambda(M)/\Lambda_0$ suggests itself, and we shall see that this is indeed the case. However, an imitation of the proof of V, Theorem 3.4 does not succeed, since the dimension of the set of singular elements in M is in general too large. Also the coset space $K_o/(K_o)^A$, which is the analogue of G/T in the Lie group case, is in general not simply connected.

Let M be semisimple, and let $\mathfrak{P}$ be a component of $\mathfrak{A} \setminus D$ containing the origin in its closure, and let $\Omega \cong \Lambda(M)/\Lambda_0$ be the subgroup of $\Lambda(M) \cdot W$ leaving $\mathfrak{P}$ fixed (see V, Theorem 2.9).

PROPOSITION 2.5. a) <u>The set</u> M_{sing} <u>of singular elements in</u> M <u>is compact and</u>

$$\dim M_{sing} \leq \dim M - (1 + \min_{\lambda \in R^{(2)}} m(\lambda)) .$$

b) $(K_o/(K_o)^A) \times \mathfrak{P}$ <u>is a regular covering of</u> M_{reg} <u>with group</u> Ω <u>under the map</u>

$$p(k(K_o)^A, X) = k \operatorname{Exp} X .$$

<u>Proof</u>. a) We have $M_{sing} = \bigcup_{\lambda \in R} \varphi_\lambda((K_o/K_o^{U_\lambda}) \times U_\lambda)$ where $\varphi_\lambda(kK_o^{U_\lambda}, x) = kx$. Hence M_{sing} is compact. By Proposition 2.1, if $2\lambda \notin R$, then

$$\mathfrak{K}^{U_\lambda} = \mathfrak{K}^{\mathfrak{A}} \oplus \mathfrak{K}_\lambda .$$

Hence $\dim(K_o/K_o^{U_\lambda}) \times U_\lambda = \dim \mathfrak{K} - \dim \mathfrak{K}^{\mathfrak{A}} - \dim \mathfrak{K}_\lambda + \dim \mathfrak{A} - 1 =$ $\dim M - \dim \mathfrak{A} - m(\lambda) + \dim \mathfrak{A} - 1 = \dim M - (1 + m(\lambda))$, and the assertion follows from V, §3, 1° and 6°.

b) The proof is straightforward following the lines of the proof of V, Proposition 3.3, and is left to the reader.

§3 RELATIONS TO LIE GROUPS

1. <u>Compact Lie groups as symmetric spaces</u>

We will now show that the concepts of maximal tori, root systems, singular elements, etc., introduced so far for Lie groups and symmetric spaces coincide if $M = L^+$ is a compact

Lie group considered as symmetric space. We know $Z(M) = Z(L)$ and if we write $M = G/K$ as usual, we have $K_o = \mathrm{Int}\, L$ (IV, Proposition 4.3).

PROPOSITION 3.1. Let L be a compact connected Lie group and $M = L^+$.

a) The maximal tori of L are exactly the maximal tori of M.

b) The root systems of L and M relative to a maximal torus coincide. All roots have multiplicity two.

c) $L_{sing} = M_{sing}$; $\Lambda(L) = \Lambda(M)$.

Proof. a) The Lts of M is $\mathfrak{M} = \mathfrak{L}^+$ with the triple product $[X,Y,Z] = \frac{1}{4}[[X,Y],Z]$ (see II, §2, (5)). It suffices to show that an abelian sub-Lts of $\mathfrak{L}^+$ is an abelian subalgebra of $\mathfrak{L}$. This follows from

$$4([X,Y,X],Y) = ([X,Y],[X,Y])$$

and the fact that $(\ ,\ )$ is positive definite.

b) Let T be a maximal torus of L; and $\mathfrak{L}_C = \mathfrak{T}_C + \Sigma\mathfrak{L}^\alpha$ the corresponding root space decomposition. Then $\mathfrak{L}^\alpha \oplus \mathfrak{L}^{-\alpha}$ is stable under conjugation, since $\overline{\mathfrak{L}^\alpha} = \mathfrak{L}^{-\alpha}$. If we set $\mathfrak{L}_\alpha = \mathfrak{L} \cap (\mathfrak{L}^\alpha \oplus \mathfrak{L}^{-\alpha})$, we have the decomposition

$$\mathfrak{L} = \mathfrak{T} \oplus \Sigma\mathfrak{L}_\alpha \tag{1}$$

and for $H \in \mathfrak{T}$ and $X = X_+ + X_- \in \mathfrak{L}_\alpha$, where $X_\pm \in \mathfrak{L}^{\pm\alpha}$, we get by V, §1, (4)

$$(2) \quad [X,H,H] = \frac{1}{4}[H,[H,X]] = \frac{1}{4}[H, 2\pi\sqrt{-1}\alpha(H)(X_+ - X_-)] = -\pi^2\alpha(H)^2 X .$$

By Proposition 1.4, we have $\mathfrak{L}_\alpha = \mathfrak{M}_\alpha$, and the root systems coincide. Also since $\dim_{\mathbb{C}} \mathfrak{L}^\alpha = 1$, we have $m(\alpha) = \dim_{\mathbb{R}} \mathfrak{L}_\alpha = 2$.

c) The first statement follows from $T_{sing} = \bigcup_{\alpha \in R} U_\alpha$ and b), and the second from $\mathrm{Exp} = \exp$.

This shows that a number of the results of V, §1 are just special cases of the corresponding facts for symmetric spaces.

2. Relations between the roots of M and G

LEMMA 3.2. *Let $\mathfrak{L}$ be a Lie algebra with an involutive automorphism σ and $(\ ,\ )$ a positive definite bilinear form on $\mathfrak{L}$ invariant under $\mathrm{ad}\,\mathfrak{L}$ and σ . Let $\mathfrak{A}$ be a maximal abelian sub-Lts of $\mathfrak{L}_- = \{X \in \mathfrak{L}: \sigma X = -X\}$. Then $\mathfrak{A}$ is an abelian subalgebra of $\mathfrak{L}$ and every abelian subalgebra of $\mathfrak{L}$ containing $\mathfrak{A}$ is stable under σ .*

Proof. The first statement follows from $([[X,Y],X],Y) = ([X,Y],[X,Y])$. Let $\mathfrak{T} \supset \mathfrak{A}$ be abelian and $X \in \mathfrak{T}$. Then $[X - \sigma X, Y] = [X,Y] + \sigma([X,Y]) = 0$ for all $Y \in \mathfrak{A}$. Since $X - \sigma X \in \mathfrak{L}_-$, it follows that $X - \sigma X \in \mathfrak{A}$ by maximality of $\mathfrak{A}$. Hence $\sigma X \in \mathfrak{T}$.

Now let A be a maximal torus in M. Then $Q(A)$ is a torus in G, and we choose a maximal torus T of G containing $Q(A)$. Then we have $\mathfrak{A} \subset \mathfrak{T}$. By Lemma 3.2, $\mathfrak{T}$ is stable under σ, and if we decompose $\mathfrak{T} = \mathfrak{T}_+ \oplus \mathfrak{T}_-$ relative to σ, we have $\mathfrak{T}_+ = \mathfrak{T} \cap \mathfrak{K}$ and $\mathfrak{T}_- = \mathfrak{A}$. Let $R(M)$ and $R(G)$ denote the root systems associated with (M,A) and (G,T). For any linear form α on $\mathfrak{T}$, let $\bar{\alpha} = 2\alpha|\mathfrak{A}$. The decomposition $\mathfrak{T} = \mathfrak{T}_+ \oplus \mathfrak{T}_-$ gives rise to a decomposition $\mathfrak{T}' = \mathfrak{T}'_+ \oplus \mathfrak{T}'_-$ of the dual, and we have, since $(\sigma(\alpha))(X) = \alpha(\sigma(X))$,

$$\bar{\alpha} = \alpha - \sigma(\alpha) . \tag{3}$$

PROPOSITION 3.3. a) T <u>and</u> $R(G)$ <u>are stable under</u> σ.

b) <u>For</u> $\lambda \in R(M)$, <u>we have</u>

$$\mathfrak{G}^\lambda = \sum_{\bar{\alpha}=\lambda} \mathfrak{G}^\alpha$$

<u>and</u>

$$(\mathfrak{K}^{\mathfrak{A}})_C = (\mathfrak{T} \cap \mathfrak{K})_C \oplus \sum_{\bar{\alpha}=0} \mathfrak{G}^\alpha .$$

<u>Hence</u> $R(M) = \{\bar{\alpha} : \alpha \in R(G)$ and $\bar{\alpha} \neq 0\}$ <u>and the multiplicity of</u> $\lambda \in R(M)$ <u>is the number of roots</u> α <u>in</u> $R(G)$ <u>such that</u> $\bar{\alpha} = \lambda$.

c) <u>If</u> $\alpha \in R(G)$ <u>then</u> $\alpha + \sigma(\alpha) \notin R(G)$.

d) $(T \cap K)_0$ <u>is a maximal torus in</u> $(K_0^A)_0$ <u>with root system</u>

$$R_0 = \{\alpha \in R(G) : \bar{\alpha} = 0\} .$$

Proof. a) As noted already, we have $\sigma(\mathfrak{T}) = \mathfrak{T}$; thus $\sigma(T) = T$. It follows that σ leaves the root space decomposition $\mathfrak{G}_C = \mathfrak{T}_C + \Sigma\, \mathfrak{G}^\alpha$ of $\mathfrak{G}_C$ invariant, and therefore also the root system $R(G)$.

b) This follows by comparing (4) and (5) of §1 in Chapter V and VI.

c) Let $E_\alpha \in \mathfrak{G}^\alpha$. Then $\sigma E_\alpha \in \mathfrak{G}^{\sigma\alpha}$. If $\alpha + \sigma(\alpha) \in R(G)$, then it vanishes on $\mathfrak{A}$. Therefore by a) and V, Theorem 4.2, $0 \neq [E_\alpha, \sigma(E_\alpha)] \in (\mathfrak{K}^{\mathfrak{A}})_C$. But $\sigma([E_\alpha, \sigma(E_\alpha)]) = [\sigma(E_\alpha), E_\alpha] = -[E_\alpha, \sigma(E_\alpha)]$, hence $[E_\alpha, \sigma(E_\alpha)] \in \mathfrak{M}_C$, a contradiction.

d) This follows immediately from the decomposition of $(\mathfrak{K}^{\mathfrak{A}})_C$ in a).

3. Spaces of symmetric elements

Let L be a compact connected Lie group with an involutive automorphism σ , and let $M = L_\sigma = \{x\sigma(x)^{-1} \colon x \in L\}$ be the space of symmetric elements in L (see IV, §4, 2). Let A be a maximal torus in M . By Lemma 3.2, $\mathfrak{A}$ is an abelian subalgebra of $\mathfrak{L}$. Hence A is a torus in L , and we choose a maximal torus T of L containing A . Then T is stable under σ (Lemma 3.2). We denote by $R(L), D(L), \Lambda(L), \ldots$ the root system, diagram, unit lattice, ..., of L relative to T and by $R(M)$, $D(M)$, $\Lambda(M)$, ..., the corresponding objects for M relative to A .

THEOREM 3.4. a) The root system $R(M)$ is the set of all nonzero linear forms $\alpha|\mathfrak{A}$ where $\alpha \in R(L)$. The center of M is $Z(M) = Z(L) \cap M$.

b) Let L be semisimple. Then M is semisimple and the lattices $\Lambda_0(M), \Lambda(M), \Lambda_1(M)$ are the intersections with $\mathfrak{A}$ of the corresponding lattices for L.

Proof. a) Since $\sigma(T) = T$, the root system $R(L)$ is stable under σ, and we have $\sigma(\mathfrak{L}_\alpha) = \mathfrak{L}_{\sigma\alpha}$ in the decomposition $\mathfrak{L} = \mathfrak{T} \oplus \Sigma\mathfrak{L}_\alpha$ (see (1) in proof of Proposition 3.1). The Lts of M is $\mathfrak{M} = \mathfrak{L}_-$ with the product $[X,Y,Z] = \frac{1}{4}[[X,Y],Z]$ (IV, Proposition 4.4). We get a decomposition $\mathfrak{M} = \mathfrak{A} \oplus \Sigma\mathfrak{M}_\alpha$, where $\mathfrak{M}_\alpha = (\mathfrak{L}_\alpha \oplus \mathfrak{L}_{\sigma\alpha}) \cap \mathfrak{M}$; and for $X = X_\alpha + X_{\sigma\alpha} \in \mathfrak{M}_\alpha$ and $H \in \mathfrak{A}$ we have since $(\sigma\alpha)(H) = \alpha(\sigma H) = -\alpha(H)$,

$$[X,H,H] = \frac{1}{4}([H,[H,X_\alpha]] + [H,[H,X_{\sigma\alpha}]])$$
$$= -\pi^2(\alpha(H)^2 X_\alpha + (\sigma\alpha)(H)^2 X_{\sigma\alpha}) = -\pi^2\alpha(H)^2 X .$$

This proves the first statement in view of Proposition 1.4. Now if $\lambda = \alpha|\mathfrak{A} \in R(M)$, we have $U_\lambda = U_\alpha \cap A$. Then by §2, (1) and the corresponding formula for L,

$$Z(M) = \cap U_\lambda \subset \cap U_\alpha = Z(L) .$$

The other inclusion is clear from the definition of $Z(M)$.

b) If L is semisimple, $Z(L)$ is finite. Hence $Z(M)$ is finite, and M is semisimple by Lemma 2.3. It follows immediately from a) and the definitions that $\Lambda(M) = \Lambda(L) \cap \mathfrak{A}$ and $\Lambda_1(M) = \Lambda_1(L) \cap \mathfrak{A}$.

Let $\tilde{L}$ be the simply connected covering of L . Then $\tilde{M} = \tilde{L}_\sigma$ is a covering of M . Hence $\Lambda_0(\tilde{M}) = \Lambda_0(M)$ and by V, Theorem 3.4, we have $\Lambda(\tilde{L}) = \Lambda_0(L)$. Thus $\Lambda_0(M) \subset \Lambda(\tilde{M}) = \Lambda_0(L) \cap \mathfrak{A}$. Now let $\mathfrak{Q}$ be a connected component of $\mathfrak{A} \setminus D(M)$ (a cell in $\mathfrak{A}$) containing 0 in its closure $\bar{\mathfrak{Q}}$. Then there exists a connected component $\mathfrak{P}$ of $\mathfrak{T} \setminus D(L)$ such that $\bar{\mathfrak{Q}} \subset \bar{\mathfrak{P}}$. To see this, it suffices to prove that for $X, Y \in \bar{\mathfrak{Q}}$ the segment $\overrightarrow{XY}$ crosses no hyperplane $\alpha = n$ of $D(L)$ in its interior. If this were the case, the restriction of α to $\mathfrak{A}$ is not zero. Hence $\lambda = \alpha|\mathfrak{A} \in R(M)$ and $\overrightarrow{XY}$ crosses the hyperplane $\lambda = n$ of $D(M)$ in its interior, a contradiction. Now

$$\Lambda_0(L) \cap \mathfrak{A} \cap \bar{\mathfrak{Q}} \subset \Lambda_0(L) \cap \bar{\mathfrak{P}} = \{0\} ,$$

thus $\Lambda_0(L) \cap \mathfrak{A} = \Lambda_0(M)$ by V, Theorem 2.9.

4. Application to Lie groups and the fundamental group

THEOREM 3.5. The set of fixed points of an involutive automorphism of a compact connected simply connected Lie group is connected. The space of symmetric elements is simply connected.

Proof. By Theorem 3.4 and V, Theorem 3.4, we have for $M = L_\sigma$

$$\Lambda(L_\sigma) = \Lambda_0(L) \cap \mathfrak{U} = \Lambda_0(L_\sigma) \quad ,$$

and it follows from Proposition 2.4 c) that L_σ is simply connected. Since $L_\sigma \cong L/L^\sigma$ (IV, Proposition 4.5), L^σ is connected.

THEOREM 3.6. *Let M be a compact semisimple symmetric space. Then*

$$\pi_1(M) \cong \Lambda(M)/\Lambda_0 \ .$$

Proof. In view of Proposition 2.4 c), it suffices to show that there exists a space M' locally isomorphic with M such that $\Lambda(M') = \Lambda_0$. Let $L = \tilde{G}$ be the simply connected covering group of the group of displacements G of M. Then $M' = L_\sigma$ has the required properties.

COROLLARY. *Let $\tilde{M}$ be the simply connected space with Lie triple system $\mathfrak{M}$ and $\bar{M} = \tilde{M}/Z(\tilde{M})$. Then $\Lambda_0 = \Lambda(\tilde{M})$ and $\Lambda_1 = \Lambda(\bar{M})$, and $Z = \Lambda_1/\Lambda_0 \cong Z(\tilde{M}) \cong \pi_1(\bar{M})$.*

We remark that the set $\{x \in L\colon \sigma(x) = x^{-1}\}$ is in general not connected, even if L is simply connected.

§4 SIGNIFICANCE OF THE MULTIPLICITIES

1. Spaces of maximal rank

In this section, we assume M to be semisimple, in addition to the conventions of §1. M is called of maximal rank if $\operatorname{rank} M = \operatorname{rank} G$.

PROPOSITION 4.1. The following conditions are equivalent:

a) M is of maximal rank;

b) all roots of M have multiplicity one;

c) $\dim M = \frac{1}{2}(\dim G + \operatorname{rank} G)$;

d) $\dim M - \dim K = \operatorname{rank} G$.

Let A be a maximal torus in M . If M is of maximal rank, then $Q(A)$ is a maximal torus in G , and $R(M) = 2R(G)$.

Proof. Let A be a maximal torus in M and $\mathfrak{G}_C = \mathfrak{A}_C \oplus (\mathfrak{K}^{\mathfrak{A}})_C \oplus \Sigma \mathfrak{G}^{\lambda}$ the corresponding decomposition (see Proposition 1.3). If M is of maximal rank, then $\mathfrak{A}$ is maximal abelian in $\mathfrak{G}$. Hence $\mathfrak{K}^{\mathfrak{A}} = 0$, and a comparison of (4) in §1 of Chapters V and VI yields $R(M) = 2R(G)$. Also $m(\lambda) = \dim \mathfrak{G}^{\lambda} = 1$ by V, Theorem 1.6. Conversely, let $m(\lambda) = 1$ for all roots λ of M . Then $\dim \mathfrak{M}_{\lambda} = \dim \mathfrak{K}_{\lambda} = 1$ in the decomposition (8) of Proposition 1.4, and since $\mathfrak{K} = [\mathfrak{M},\mathfrak{M}]$, it follows from

Proposition 1.4 c) that $\mathfrak{K}^{\mathfrak{A}} \subset \Sigma[\mathfrak{M}_\lambda, \mathfrak{M}_\lambda] = 0$. Hence $\mathfrak{A} = \mathfrak{G}^{\mathfrak{A}}$ is maximal abelian in $\mathfrak{G}$ and M is of maximal rank. The equivalence of b), c) and d) is now evident from Proposition 1.4.

THEOREM 4.2. _Let_ L _be a compact connected semisimple Lie group and_ T _a maximal torus in_ L . _Then there exists an involutive automorphism_ σ _of_ L _such that_ $\sigma(x) = x^{-1}$ _for all_ $x \in T$. _Any two such automorphisms are conjugate by an inner automorphism of_ L .

Proof. By V, Theorem 4.4 a), the map $X \to -X$ of $\mathfrak{T}$ can be extended to an automorphism σ of L . Let $\mathfrak{L}_C = \mathfrak{T}_C \oplus \Sigma \mathfrak{L}^\alpha$ be the usual decomposition and $E_\alpha \in \mathfrak{L}^\alpha$. Then $\sigma(\mathfrak{L}^\alpha) = \mathfrak{L}^{-\alpha}$; hence $\sigma(E_\alpha) = z_\alpha E_{-\alpha}$ and $\sigma^2(E_\alpha) = z_\alpha z_{-\alpha} E_\alpha$. Now $[\mathfrak{T}, [E_\alpha, E_{-\alpha}]] = 0$ shows $[E_\alpha, E_{-\alpha}] \in \mathfrak{T}_C$, and it is easily seen that $[E_\alpha, E_{-\alpha}]$ is a nonzero multiple of $\vec{\alpha}$. From $-[E_\alpha, E_{-\alpha}] = \sigma([E_\alpha, E_{-\alpha}]) = z_\alpha z_{-\alpha}[E_{-\alpha}, E_\alpha]$, it follows $z_\alpha z_{-\alpha} = 1$ and σ is involutive.

Now let τ be an involutive automorphism such that $\tau(y) = y^{-1}$ for all y in a maximal torus T' . Then T and T' are conjugate by an element $g \in L$. If we replace τ by $\mathrm{Ad}g \circ \tau \circ \mathrm{Ad}g^{-1}$, we may assume then that $\tau(x) = x^{-1}$ for all $x \in T$. Let B be a basis for the root system R , and choose $X, Y \in \mathfrak{T}$ such that $\sigma(E_\alpha) = e^{2\pi\sqrt{-1}\,\alpha(X)} \overline{E}_\alpha$ and

$\tau(E_\alpha) = e^{2\pi\sqrt{-1}\,\alpha(Y)}\overline{E_\alpha}$ for all $\alpha \in B$. Since $\sigma(\mathfrak{L}^\alpha) = \mathfrak{L}^{-\alpha} = \overline{\mathfrak{L}^\alpha}$ and $\sigma(E_\alpha) = z_\alpha \overline{E_\alpha}$ with $|z_\alpha| = 1$, this is possible. Then, putting $\varphi = \mathrm{Ad}\exp\frac{1}{2}(X - Y)$, we have

$$\varphi(\sigma(E_\alpha)) = e^{2\pi\sqrt{-1}(-\alpha(\frac{X-Y}{2})+\alpha(X))}\overline{E_\alpha}$$

and

$$\tau(\varphi(E_\alpha)) = e^{2\pi\sqrt{-1}(\alpha(Y)+\alpha(\frac{X-Y}{2}))}\overline{E_\alpha}\,.$$

Passing to the complex conjugate, we see that $\varphi \circ \sigma$ and $\tau \circ \varphi$ coincide also on $\overline{E_\alpha}$, $\alpha \in B$, and since $\mathfrak{T}$ and the E_α, $\overline{E_\alpha}$ generate $\mathfrak{L}_C$ (V, Theorem 4.2), it follows $\tau = \varphi \circ \sigma \circ \varphi^{-1}$.

Let σ be as above, and L_σ the corresponding space of symmetric elements. Then $T \subset L_\sigma$ is a maximal torus of L_σ, and the root systems of L and L_σ coincide. Also the lattices Λ coincide for L and L_σ and $Z(L) = Z(L_\sigma)$ (Theorem 3.4). It follows that $L \to L_\sigma$ establishes a <u>one-to-one correspondence between the isomorphism classes of compact semisimple Lie groups and compact semisimple symmetric spaces of maximal rank</u>.

We finally remark that the spaces of maximal rank correspond under duality to the <u>normal real forms</u> of complex semisimple Lie algebras. If $\mathfrak{G}_o = \mathfrak{K} \oplus \mathfrak{P}$ is a Cartan decomposition of the real semisimple Lie algebra $\mathfrak{G}_o$, then $\mathfrak{G}_o$ is called a normal real form of its complexification $\mathfrak{G}_C$ if $\mathfrak{P}$ contains a maximal abelian subalgebra of $\mathfrak{G}_o$. It is then clear that

$\mathfrak{G} = \mathfrak{K} \oplus \mathfrak{M}$ belongs to a symmetric space of maximal rank if and only if the dual $\mathfrak{G}^* = \mathfrak{K} \oplus \mathfrak{M}^*$ is a normal real form. From Theorem 4.2, one deduces easily that every complex semisimple Lie algebra has a normal real form which is unique up to isomorphism.

2. Spaces of splitting rank

Let M be as above. M is said to be of splitting rank if $\operatorname{rank} G = \operatorname{rank} K + \operatorname{rank} M$.

THEOREM 4.3. M is of splitting rank if and only if all roots have even multiplicity.

Proof. We use the notations of Proposition 3.3. Let $\lambda \in R(M)$ and $m(\lambda)$ odd. For any $\alpha \in R(G)$ we have $\overline{-\sigma(\alpha)} = \bar{\alpha}$. Assume $-\sigma(\alpha) = \alpha$ and $-\sigma(\beta) = \beta$ and $\bar{\alpha} = \bar{\beta}$. Then $\alpha | \mathfrak{K} \cap \mathfrak{T} = 0 = \beta | \mathfrak{K} \cap \mathfrak{T}$ shows $\alpha = \beta$. It follows that there exists exactly one $\alpha \in R(G)$ such that $\bar{\alpha} = \lambda$ and $-\sigma(\alpha) = \alpha$. Then $\sigma(\mathfrak{G}^{\alpha}) = \mathfrak{G}^{-\alpha} = \overline{\mathfrak{G}^{\alpha}}$ (see V, Proposition 1.4) and the map $Z \to \sigma(\bar{Z})$ is an involutive $\mathbb{R}$-linear map of $\mathfrak{G}^{\alpha}$ onto itself (here $\bar{Z}$ is the complex conjugate of $Z \in \mathfrak{G}_C$ relative to the real form $\mathfrak{G}$). If $\mathfrak{G}^{\alpha} = \mathfrak{G}^{\alpha}_{+} \oplus \mathfrak{G}^{\alpha}_{-}$ is the (± 1)-eigenspace decomposition, we have $\mathfrak{G}^{\alpha}_{-} = \sqrt{-1}\mathfrak{G}^{\alpha}_{+}$. Hence $\mathfrak{G}^{\alpha}_{+} \neq 0$, and for $0 \neq E_{\alpha} = X_{\alpha} + \sqrt{-1}Y_{\alpha} \in \mathfrak{G}^{\alpha}_{+}$, we have $0 \neq X_\alpha \in \mathfrak{K}_\lambda$. Since $[H, E_\alpha] = 2\pi\sqrt{-1}\alpha(H)E_\alpha = 0$ for $H \in \mathfrak{K} \cap \mathfrak{T}$, it follows that $[\mathfrak{K} \cap \mathfrak{T}, X_\alpha] = 0$, and $X_\alpha \notin \mathfrak{K} \cap \mathfrak{T}$ since $X_\alpha \in \mathfrak{K}_\lambda$. Hence $\mathfrak{K} \cap \mathfrak{T}$ is not maximal abelian in $\mathfrak{K}$, and M is not of splitting rank.

Now let $m(\lambda)$ be even for all $\lambda \in R(M)$. From the considerations above, we see that then $-\sigma(\alpha) \neq \alpha$ and hence $\alpha | \mathfrak{K} \cap \mathfrak{T} \neq 0$ for all $\alpha \in R(G)$. The subspace $\mathfrak{J}_\alpha = \mathfrak{G}^\alpha + \mathfrak{G}^{-\alpha} + \mathfrak{G}^{\sigma(\alpha)} + \mathfrak{G}^{-\sigma(\alpha)}$ of $\mathfrak{G}_C$ is stable under σ and complex conjugation . It follows that

$$\mathfrak{K} = \mathfrak{K} \cap \mathfrak{T} \oplus \Sigma\, \mathfrak{K} \cap \mathfrak{J}_\alpha .$$

Then we have for $H \in \mathfrak{K} \cap \mathfrak{T}$ and $X = X_\alpha + X_{-\alpha} + X_{\sigma(\alpha)} + X_{-\sigma(\alpha)} \in \mathfrak{K} \cap \mathfrak{J}_\alpha$:

$$[H, X] = 2\pi\sqrt{-1}\,\alpha(H)(X_\alpha - X_{-\alpha} + X_{\sigma(\alpha)} - X_{-\sigma(\alpha)}) ,$$

and this implies

$$[H, [H, X]] = -4\pi^2 \alpha(H)^2 X .$$

It follows that $\mathfrak{K} \cap \mathfrak{T}$ is maximal abelian in $\mathfrak{K}$, which completes the proof.

3. Characterization of Lie groups among symmetric spaces

THEOREM 4.4. Let M be a compact semisimple symmetric space. The following statements are equivalent.

a) M is a Lie group considered as symmetric space;

b) <u>all roots of M have multiplicity two</u>;

c) $\mathfrak{G}^*$ <u>has a complex structure</u>.

<u>Proof</u>. The implications a) $\to$ b) and a) $\to$ c) have been proved in Proposition 3.1 and IV, Theorem 1.9. For the converse, we remark that it suffices to show that $\mathfrak{M}$ is a Lie algebra $\mathfrak{L}$ considered as Lts. Indeed, if this is the case, the simply connected covering space $\tilde{M}$ is a Lie group, and $M = \tilde{M}/F$ where F is a subgroup of the center of $\tilde{M}$. Since the centers of $\tilde{M}$ as Lie group and symmetric space coincide, it follows that M is a Lie group. Thus c) implies a) by IV, Theorem 1.9.

Let b) be satisfied. If $\mathfrak{M} = \mathfrak{M}_1 \oplus \mathfrak{M}_2$ is a decomposition in ideals, then $\mathfrak{M}_i \cap \mathfrak{A}$ is maximal abelian in $\mathfrak{M}_i$; hence we have a corresponding decomposition of the root system. Thus we may assume $\mathfrak{M}$ to be simple, and by IV, Proposition 1.2, we have to show that $\mathfrak{G}$ is not simple. By Proposition 3.3, for every $\lambda \in R(M)$ there are exactly two roots $\alpha, \beta \in R(G)$ such that $\lambda = \bar{\alpha} = \bar{\beta}$. Now $\overline{-\sigma(\alpha)} = \bar{\alpha}$ implies $-\sigma(\alpha) = \alpha$ or $-\sigma(\alpha) = \beta$. But we cannot have $-\sigma(\alpha) = \alpha$, since then also $-\sigma(\beta) = \beta$, which would imply $0 = \alpha|\mathfrak{T} \cap \mathfrak{K} = \beta|\mathfrak{T} \cap \mathfrak{K}$, and hence $\alpha = \beta$. It follows $-\sigma(\alpha) = \beta$. Now by Proposition 3.3, $\alpha + \sigma(\alpha) = \alpha - \beta \notin R(G)$, therefore $(\alpha, \beta) \leq 0$ (V, Lemma 2.1). Assume $(\alpha, \beta) < 0$. Then $\alpha + \beta \in R(G)$, hence $2\lambda = \overline{\alpha + \beta} \in R(M)$. Now

$-\sigma(\alpha+\beta)=\alpha+\beta$, which, as we just saw, is impossible. This shows $(\alpha,\beta)=0$.

Now let $\gamma \in R(G)$ and $\bar{\gamma}=0$. Then, if $(\alpha,\gamma)<0$, we have $\alpha+\gamma \in R(G)$ and $\bar{\alpha}=\overline{\alpha+\gamma}$; hence $\alpha+\gamma=\beta$ or $\beta-\alpha \in R(G)$, contradiction. Similarly, if $(\alpha,\gamma)>0$, $\alpha-\gamma=\beta$ and $\alpha-\beta=\gamma \in R(G)$, which is impossible. This shows that

$$R(G)=\{\gamma\colon\ \bar{\gamma}=0\} \cup \{\alpha\colon\ \bar{\alpha}\neq 0\}$$

is a decomposition in two orthogonal subsets. By Proposition 3.3, the ideal of $\mathfrak{G}$ corresponding to $R_0=\{\gamma\colon\ \bar{\gamma}=0\}$ is contained in $\mathfrak{K}$ and hence zero. It follows $R_0=\emptyset$ and $\bar{\alpha}\neq 0$ for all $\alpha \in R(G)$.

Let $\mathfrak{C}$ be a Weyl chamber in $\mathfrak{A}$. Then every root of G restricted to $\mathfrak{C}$ is either positive or negative, therefore $\mathfrak{C}$ is contained in a Weyl chamber $\mathfrak{D}$ of $\mathfrak{T}$. Moreover, if α is positive on $\mathfrak{D}$, then $-\sigma(\alpha)|\mathfrak{C}=\alpha|\mathfrak{C}$ is positive. Hence $-\sigma(\mathfrak{D})=\mathfrak{D}$ and $-\sigma(B)=B$ where B is the basis of R(G) belonging to $\mathfrak{D}$ (V, Theorem 2.2).

We are now going to show that B is decomposable, which is sufficient by V, Proposition 4.1 and Theorem 4.4. To do this, we need the following:

LEMMA 4.5. <u>Let</u> B <u>be a basis for the root system</u> R . <u>A chain in</u> B <u>is a subset</u> $\{\alpha_1,\ldots,\alpha_k\}$ <u>such that</u> $(\alpha_i,\alpha_{i+1})\neq 0$. <u>Then</u>

a) B *is indecomposable if and only if any two elements of* B *can be joined by a chain.*

b) B *does not contain cycles, i.e., chains such that* $(\alpha_k, \alpha_1) \neq 0$ *and* $k > 2$.

Proof. a) This is immediate from the definitions.

b) Let $\beta_i = \alpha_i / \|\alpha_i\|$. Then

$$(2(\beta_i, \beta_j))^2 = 2 \frac{(\alpha_i, \alpha_j)}{(\alpha_i, \alpha_i)} \cdot 2 \frac{(\alpha_i, \alpha_j)}{(\alpha_j, \alpha_j)} = 0, 1, 2, 3$$

by the table in V, §2 . If $2(\beta_i, \beta_j)$ is not zero, then it is ≤ -1 . It follows that

$$0 < (\Sigma\beta_i, \Sigma\beta_i) = k + 2 \sum_{i<j} (\beta_i, \beta_j)$$

is only possible for $k \leq 2$.

We now complete the proof of Theorem 4.4. Let $\alpha \in B$, and suppose that there is a chain $\{\alpha_o, \ldots, \alpha_{r+1}\}$ of roots in B connecting $\alpha = \alpha_o$ with $-\sigma(\alpha) = \alpha_{r+1}$. Take the smallest $i \geq 1$ such that $-\sigma(\alpha_i) = \alpha_j \in \{\alpha_o, \ldots, \alpha_r\}$. Then $\{\alpha_{j+1}, \ldots, \alpha_{r+1}, -\sigma(\alpha_1), \ldots, -\sigma(\alpha_i)\}$ is a cycle in B . It follows $j = r$ and $i = 1$, or $-\sigma(\alpha_1) = \alpha_r$. Continuing in this way, we end up with a root β such that $-\sigma(\beta) = \beta$ or $-\sigma(\beta) = \gamma$ and $(\beta, \gamma) \neq 0$, a contradiction.

NOTES

§1 The emphasis here is put on introducing the roots of M intrinsically and not as restrictions of roots of G (see Proposition 3.3). The treatment follows Helgason [1], [2].

§2 Here the results are strictly analogous to those for Lie groups (V, §1) and indeed contain them as special cases. The proofs however are more computational in character. The simplest example where

$$\dim M_{\text{sing}} = \dim M - 2$$

is the sphere S^2 ; there M_{sing} consists of two antipodal points. In Proposition 2.5 a), we have actually equality. It should be noted that a point being regular or singular depends upon the choice of the base point. In contrast to the Lie group case, the centralizer K_o^A of a maximal torus is in general not connected. The component group has been determined by Araki [2] in the simply connected case; it is $(\mathbb{Z}_2)^p$ where p is the number of roots of multiplicity one in a basis of the root system of M .

§3, 4 Proposition 3.1 is remarkable insofar as it shows that the root system of a Lie group is really a property of the symmetric space, and it is the multiplicities which distinguish Lie groups among symmetric spaces (Theorem 4.4). Theorem 3.4 is contained in Bott-Samelson [1]. Theorem 3.5 and 3.6 go back to É. Cartan [2]. Theorem 4.3 is due to Araki [2].

CHAPTER VII

CLASSIFICATION

§1 PREPARATIONS

1. Reduction of the problem

In this chapter, we will classify the Riemannian symmetric spaces. Let M be such a space. By IV, Theorem 1.6, the simply connected covering space $\tilde{M}$ is a direct product $M_o \times M_+ \times M_-$ where M_o is Euclidean and $M_\pm$ is of (non-)compact type. Also by IV, Theorem 4.2, $M = \tilde{M}/F$ where F is a discrete subgroup of the center $Z(\tilde{M})$ of $\tilde{M}$. Clearly, $Z(\tilde{M}) = Z(M_o) \times Z(M_+) \times Z(M_-)$ and $Z(M_o) = M_o$ and $Z(M_+)$ is trivial by IV, Theorem 2.4. Thus $Z(\tilde{M}) = M_o \times Z(M_-)$, and the problem reduces to: find all simply connected spaces of (non-)compact type and their centers. Since we have a one-to-one correspondence between the compact and the noncompact type under duality (IV, §1, 3), it suffices to find all simply connected compact spaces and their centers. By II, Theorem 4.12, the classification of simply connected spaces is equivalent to the classification of Lie triple systems, and by VI, Corollary of Theorem 3.6, we can determine the center of the simply connected space from its root system. We have thus reduced our problem to a purely algebraic one: determine all Lts of compact type and their root systems.

Let $\mathfrak{M}$ be such a Lts and M the corresponding simply connected space. Decompose M into simple (= irreducible, IV, Corollary 2 of Theorem 1.6) factors corresponding to the decomposition of $\mathfrak{M}$ into its simple ideals (IV, Proposition 1.3). Clearly the center of M is the product of the centers of the simple factors; hence we may assume $\mathfrak{M}$ to be simple. Let $\mathfrak{G} = \mathfrak{K} \oplus \mathfrak{M}$ be the standard imbedding of $\mathfrak{M}$. By IV, Proposition 1.2, either $\mathfrak{M}$ is a simple Lie algebra considered as Lts, or $\mathfrak{G}$ is simple. In the latter case, let σ be the automorphism of $\mathfrak{G}$ which is $+\mathrm{id}$ on $\mathfrak{K}$ on $-\mathrm{id}$ on $\mathfrak{M}$, and let σ' be another involutive automorphism of $\mathfrak{G}$ and $\mathfrak{G} = \mathfrak{K}' \oplus \mathfrak{M}'$ the (± 1)-eigenspace decomposition relative to σ'. If σ and σ' are conjugate by an automorphism of $\mathfrak{G}$, then clearly $\mathfrak{M}$ and $\mathfrak{M}'$ are isomorphic. Conversely, an isomorphism between $\mathfrak{M}$ and $\mathfrak{M}'$ extends to an automorphism of $\mathfrak{G}$ since $\mathfrak{G}$ is the standard imbedding of $\mathfrak{M}$ and $\mathfrak{M}'$, and therefore σ and σ' are conjugate by this automorphism. Hence the classification of simple Lts of compact type reduces to

i) find all compact simple Lie algebras;

ii) find all involutive automorphisms of compact simple Lie algebras, up to conjugacy.

By V, Theorem 4.4, problem i) is equivalent with the classification of reduced root systems. We will assume its solution as known (see 3). The determination of the root systems in case ii) is more difficult.

The classification of Lts of compact type is connected with that of real simple Lie algebras by

THEOREM 1.1. *Let* $\mathfrak{M}$ *be a simple Lie triple system of compact type and* $\mathfrak{G}^* = \mathfrak{K} \oplus \mathfrak{M}^*$ *the standard imbedding of its dual. Then* $\mathfrak{M} \to \mathfrak{G}^*$ *establishes a one-to-one correspondence between the isomorphism classes of simple Lie triple systems of compact type and noncompact real simple Lie algebras. Under this correspondence, the compact simple Lie algebras* (considered as Lie triple systems) *correspond to the complex simple Lie algebras* (considered as real Lie algebras).

Proof. This follows easily from the existence and uniqueness of Cartan decompositions and IV, Theorem 1.9.

2. Dynkin diagrams

Let R be a root system and B a basis of R. With B we associate its Dynkin diagram Δ as follows. Choose vertices o corresponding to the elements of B (we identify B with the set of these vertices). Connect α and β by $\alpha(\beta^*).\beta(\alpha^*)$ lines (recall that $\alpha(\beta^*).\beta(\alpha^*) = \cos^2\theta = 0,1,2,3$ by V, §2). If $\|\alpha\| > \|\beta\|$, indicate the direction from α to β by an arrow. If $\alpha \in B$ and $2\alpha \in R$, indicate this by ⊚.

Notice that Δ depends only on R, since any two bases are conjugate under the Weyl group. It also follows from VI, Lemma 4.5 a) that R is indecomposable if and only if Δ is connected.

PROPOSITION 1.2. a) A root system is uniquely determined by its Dynkin diagram.

b) The group $E = \mathrm{Aut}\ R/W$ is isomorphic with the group of symmetries of the Dynkin diagram.

Proof. a) It follows from the definition of a basis that $\alpha - \beta \notin R$ for $\alpha,\beta \in B$. Hence by V, Lemma 2.1, $\beta(\alpha^*) \leq 0$. Since we know from Δ whether $\|\alpha\| \leq \|\beta\|$ or $\|\alpha\| \geq \|\beta\|$, the number of lines in Δ connecting α and β determines $\beta(\alpha^*)$ (see the table in V, §2). Now let R_i be root systems for V_i with bases B_i $(i=1, 2)$ giving rise to the same Dynkin diagram. Then there exists a bijection $\varphi\colon B_1 \to B_2$ such that $\varphi(\beta)(\varphi(\alpha)^*) = \beta(\alpha^*)$ for all $\alpha, \beta \in B_1$. Extend φ to a linear isomorphism $\varphi\colon V_1' \to V_2'$ by linearity (V_i' is the dual of V_i). Then

$$s_{\varphi(\alpha)}(\varphi(\beta)) = \varphi(\beta) - \varphi(\beta)(\varphi(\alpha)^*)\varphi(\alpha) = \varphi(\beta) - \beta(\alpha^*)\varphi(\alpha) = \varphi(s_\alpha(\beta))$$

for $\alpha, \beta \in B_1$, hence $s_{\varphi(\alpha)} \circ \varphi = \varphi \circ s_\alpha$ for all $\alpha \in B_1$. Since the Weyl group is generated by the reflections in the simple roots and every root is of the form $w(\alpha)$ or $2w(\alpha)$ where α is simple, it follows that $\varphi(R_1) = R_2$.

b) It follows from the proof above that every symmetry of Δ can be extended to an automorphism of R leaving the Weyl chamber $\mathfrak{C}$ corresponding to B invariant. Conversely, every automorphism of R leaving $\mathfrak{C}$ invariant induces a symmetry of Δ. Now by V, Lemma 2.5 and Theorem 2.9, $\operatorname{Aut} R = W \cdot \Phi$ where Φ is the subgroup of $\operatorname{Aut} R$ leaving $\mathfrak{C}$ invariant. This finishes the proof.

An effective method for enumerating the roots from Δ can be found in Jacobson [1], p. 122.

3. Classification of root systems

The following table gives the result of the classification of reduced root systems and the corresponding compact

R	Δ	$\mathfrak{G}$	$\tilde{G}$	dim $\mathfrak{G}$
A_n	o—o—...—o	$\mathfrak{SU}(n+1)$	$SU(n+1)$	$(n+1)^2-1$
B_n	o—o—...—o$\Rightarrow$o	$\mathfrak{SO}(2n+1)$	$Spin(2n+1)$	$2n^2+n$
C_n	o—o—...—o$\Leftarrow$o	$\mathfrak{Sp}(n)$	$Sp(n)$	$2n^2+n$
D_n	o—o—...—o$<^o_o$	$\mathfrak{SO}(2n)$	$Spin(2n)$	$2n^2-n$
G_2	o$\Lleftarrow$o	$\mathfrak{G}_2$	$\underline{\underline{G}}_2$	14
F_4	o—o$\Leftarrow$o—o	$\mathfrak{F}_4$	$\underline{\underline{F}}_4$	52
E_6	o—o—o—o—o / o	$\mathfrak{E}_6$	$\underline{\underline{E}}_6$	78
E_7	o—o—o—o—o—o / o	$\mathfrak{E}_7$	$\underline{\underline{E}}_7$	133
E_8	o—o—o—o—o—o—o / o	$\mathfrak{E}_8$	$\underline{\underline{E}}_8$	248

Table 1

Lie algebras. The index n in A_n , B_n , etc., is the rank
of the root system = number of vertices in the Dynkin diagram.
The notations for the classical groups are explained in §2, $\underline{\underline{1}}$.

We remark that $\mathfrak{G}_2$ is the Lie algebra of derivations of
the Cayley division algebra $\mathbb{O}$ and $\underline{\underline{G}}_2$ its group of automorphisms. Also $\mathfrak{F}_4$ is the derivation algebra of the excep-
tional Jordan algebra $\mathfrak{G} = \mathfrak{K}(3,\mathbb{O})$ of 3×3 Hermitian matrices
over $\mathbb{O}$ and $\underline{\underline{F}}_4$ its automorphism group. $\mathfrak{E}_6$ can be realized

as $\mathfrak{F}_4 \oplus \sqrt{-1}\,\mathfrak{A}_0$ where $\mathfrak{A}_0$ are the elements of trace 0 in $\mathfrak{A}$. The table is complete and contains no repetitions with the following restrictions: A_n: $n \geq 1$; B_n: $n \geq 2$; C_n: $n \geq 3$; D_n: $n \geq 4$. In the lower dimensions there are the following isomorphisms:

$$A_1 = B_1 = C_1 \; ; \quad \mathfrak{SU}(2) \cong \mathfrak{SO}(3) \cong \mathfrak{Sp}(1) \; ;$$

$$B_2 = C_2 \; ; \quad \mathfrak{SO}(5) \cong \mathfrak{Sp}(2) \; ;$$

$$D_2 = A_1 \times A_1 \; ; \quad \mathfrak{SO}(4) \cong \mathfrak{SO}(3) \times \mathfrak{SO}(3) \; ;$$

$$D_3 = A_3 \; ; \quad \mathfrak{SO}(6) \cong \mathfrak{SU}(4) \; .$$

Occasionally, the notations $\mathfrak{A}_n = \mathfrak{SU}(n+1)$, $\mathfrak{B}_n = \mathfrak{SO}(2n+1)$, $\mathfrak{C}_n = \mathfrak{Sp}(n)$, $\mathfrak{D}_n = \mathfrak{SO}(2n)$ will also be used.

A proof of the classification can be found in Jacobson [1].

PROPOSITION 1.3. <u>The non-reduced indecomposable root systems and their Dynkin diagrams are given by</u>

BC_1: ◎

BC_n: o—o—...—o⇒◎ $(n \geq 2)$

<u>Proof</u>. Let R be a nonreduced indecomposable root system. If R has rank one, then obviously $R = \{\pm\alpha, \pm 2\alpha\}$; thus we assume rank $R > 1$. Let $R^{(1)} = \{\alpha \in R: \frac{\alpha}{2} \notin R\}$. Then $R^{(1)}$ is reduced and indecomposable and a basis B of $R^{(1)}$ is also a basis of R (see V, Proposition 2.4). By the Corollary

of this Proposition, there is $\alpha \in B$ such that $2\alpha \in R$, or else R would be reduced. For all $\beta \in R$, we have $\beta(\alpha^*) \in \mathbb{Z}$ and $\beta((2\alpha)^*) = \frac{1}{2}\beta(\alpha^*) \in \mathbb{Z}$. Hence $\beta(\alpha^*)$ is even. Now let $\beta \in B$ and $\beta(\alpha^*) \neq 0$. Then $\beta(\alpha^*) = -2$; hence the Dynkin diagram Δ' of B contains a figure $\beta\ \text{o}\!\Rightarrow\!\text{o}\ \alpha$. Moreover, α is an endpoint of Δ' or else a figure $\text{o}\!\Rightarrow\!\text{o}\!\Leftarrow\!\text{o}$ would occur, which is impossible by Table 1. This shows that $R^{(1)} = B_n$ and $\Delta' = \text{o}\!-\!\text{o}\!-\!\ldots\!-\!\text{o}\!\Rightarrow\!\underset{\alpha}{\text{o}}$. The consideration above shows also that $2\gamma \notin R$ for all $\gamma \neq \alpha$ in B. This completes the proof.

We give next an explicit construction of the root systems of "classical type". The verifications are left to the reader as an exercise. We denote by $e_1, \ldots, e_n$ the usual basis of $\mathbb{R}^n$ and by $\epsilon_1, \ldots, \epsilon_n$ its dual basis, i.e., the linear forms defined by $\epsilon_i(e_k) = \delta_{ik}$.

A_n: Let V be the hyperplane $\sum_{i=1}^{n+1} \epsilon_i = 0$ in $\mathbb{R}^{n+1}$. Then

$$R = \{(\epsilon_i - \epsilon_j)|V : i,j = 1,\ldots,n+1 ,\ i \neq j\} .$$

The inverse root of $(\epsilon_i - \epsilon_j)|V$ is $e_i - e_j$. A basis is given by $(\epsilon_1 - \epsilon_2)|V, \ldots, (\epsilon_n - \epsilon_{n+1})|V$.

B_n: Here $V = \mathbb{R}^n$ and $R = \{\pm\epsilon_i , \pm\epsilon_i \pm \epsilon_j : i \neq j\}$. The inverse roots are given by $\epsilon_i^* = 2e_i$, $(\epsilon_i \pm \epsilon_j)^* = e_i \pm e_j$. A basis is given by $\epsilon_1 - \epsilon_2 , \epsilon_2 - \epsilon_3 , \ldots , \epsilon_{n-1} - \epsilon_n , \epsilon_n$.

C_n: Here $V = \mathbb{R}^n$ and $R = \{\pm 2\epsilon_i, \pm\epsilon_i \pm \epsilon_j : i \neq j\}$. The inverse roots are given by $(2\epsilon_i)^* = e_i$, $(\epsilon_i \pm \epsilon_j)^* = e_i \pm e_j$. A basis is given by $\epsilon_1 - \epsilon_2, \ldots, \epsilon_{n-1} - \epsilon_n, 2\epsilon_n$.

D_n: Here $V = \mathbb{R}^n$ and $R = \{\pm\epsilon_i \pm \epsilon_j : i \neq j\}$. The inverse roots are $(\epsilon_i \pm \epsilon_j)^* = e_i \pm e_j$. A basis is given by $\{\epsilon_1 - \epsilon_2, \ldots, \epsilon_{n-1} - \epsilon_n, \epsilon_{n-1} + \epsilon_n\}$.

BC_n: By Proposition 1.3, $R^{(1)} = B_n$, and by V, Proposition 2.4, we have that $\{m_\alpha \alpha : m_\alpha = 2$ if $2\alpha \in R$, $m_\alpha = 1$ otherwise, $\alpha \in B\} = \{\epsilon_1 - \epsilon_2, \ldots, \epsilon_{n-1} - \epsilon_n, 2\epsilon_n\}$ is a basis for $R^{(2)}$. Hence $R^{(2)} = C_n$, and we have $R = B_n \cup C_n = \{\pm\epsilon_i, \pm 2\epsilon_i, \pm\epsilon_i \pm \epsilon_j : i \neq j\}$.

4. Extended Dynkin diagrams

Let R be an indecomposable root system and $B = \{\alpha_1, \ldots, \alpha_n\}$ a basis of R. An enumeration of the roots shows that there is a maximal root $\omega = \sum_{i=1}^{n} m_i \alpha_i$, i.e., for every other root $\alpha = \Sigma n_i \alpha_i$, we have $n_i \leq m_i$. In particular, $m_i > 0$. Since $\alpha_i + \omega$ is not a root, we have $\omega(\alpha_i^*) \geq 0$. Let $\alpha_o = -\omega$. Construct the extended Dynkin diagram $\tilde{\Delta}$ with vertices $\{\alpha_o, \ldots, \alpha_n\}$ in the same way as Δ. If we put $m_o = 1$ and write the coefficient m_i at α_i, we get the following table. Recall that $Z = \Lambda_1/\Lambda_0$ and $E = \mathrm{Aut}\, R/W$ acts on Z (V, Proposition 2.6).

R	$\tilde{\Delta}$	R	$\tilde{\Delta}$
A_1		F_4	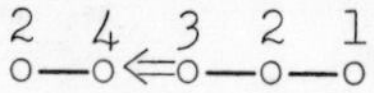
A_n $(n\geq 2)$	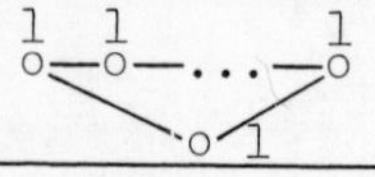	E_6	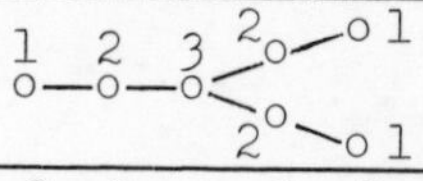
B_n $(n\geq 3)$	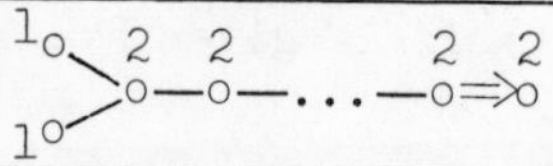	E_7	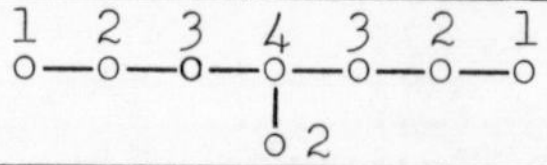
C_n $(n\geq 2)$		E_8	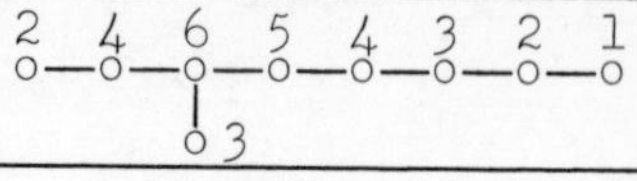
D_n $(n\geq 4)$	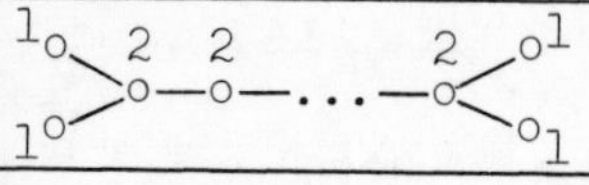	BC_1	
G_2	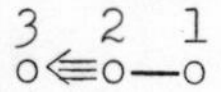	BC_n $(n\geq 2)$	

Table 2

PROPOSITION 1.4. a) Every symmetry of $\tilde{\Delta}$ is induced by an automorphism of R .

b) The order of Z equals the number of ones among $m_o,\ldots,m_n$.

c) The group $\mathrm{Aut}\,\tilde{\Delta}$ of symmetries of $\tilde{\Delta}$ is isomorphic to the semidirect product $Z\cdot E$.

Proof. a) Let π be the permutation of $\{0,1,\ldots,n\}$ corresponding to a symmetry of $\tilde{\Delta}$. Put $a_{ij}=\alpha_i(\alpha_j^*)$. Then a similar consideration as in the proof of Proposition 1.2 a) shows that $\tilde{\Delta}$ determines a_{ij} , and it follows $a_{ij}=a_{\pi(i),\pi(j)}$. We show next that $m_{\pi(i)}=m_i$. From the relation $\sum_{i=0}^{n} m_i \alpha_i = 0$, we obtain

$$\sum_{i=0}^{n} m_i a_{ij} = 0 \ . \tag{1}$$

Now the rank of the matrix (a_{ij}) is n since $\alpha_1,\ldots,\alpha_n$ are linearly independent and $a_{ij} = 2(\alpha_i,\alpha_j)/(\alpha_j,\alpha_j)$. Therefore $(m_o,\ldots,m_n)$ is up to a scalar multiple the only solution of (1). Now we have

$$0 = \Sigma m_i a_{ij} = \Sigma m_i a_{\pi^{-1}(i),\pi^{-1}(j)} ,$$

or, equivalently, $\Sigma m_{\pi(i)} a_{ij} = 0$. Hence $m_{\pi(i)} = cm_i$. But $c = 1$, since the m_i are positive integers and $m_o = 1$.

Define now a linear transformation φ by $\varphi(\alpha_i) = \alpha_{\pi(i)}$, $i = 1,\ldots,n$. Then the same argument as in the proof of Proposition 1.2 a) shows that $\varphi \in \operatorname{Aut} R$, and we have

$$\varphi(\alpha_o) = -\varphi(\sum_{i=1}^{n} m_i \alpha_i) = -\sum_{i=1}^{n} m_i \alpha_{\pi(i)} = -\sum_{i=1}^{n} m_{\pi(i)} \alpha_{\pi(i)}$$
$$= m_{\pi(o)} \alpha_{\pi(o)} = \alpha_{\pi(o)} \ .$$

Hence φ induces π on $\tilde{\Delta}$.

b) The Weyl chamber $\mathfrak{C}$ corresponding to the basis $\{\alpha_1,\ldots,\alpha_n\}$ is given by $\alpha_i > 0$, and the unique cell $\mathfrak{P}$ in $\mathfrak{C}$ containing the origin in its closure is described by

$$\alpha_i > 0 , \quad (i = 1,\ldots,n) \ ; \quad -\alpha_o < 1 \ . \tag{2}$$

Thus $\mathfrak{P}$ is a simplex. Let $X_o = 0, X_1,\ldots,X_n$ be its vertices defined by $\alpha_i(X_j) = \delta_{ij}/m_i$, $-\alpha_o(X_j) = 1$, $(i,j = 1,\ldots,n)$.

By V, Theorem 2.9, the order of Z is the number of points in $\bar{\mathfrak{P}} \cap \Lambda_1$. Now $X_j \in \Lambda_1$ if and only if $m_j = 1$, and our assertion follows.

c) Let Ψ (resp. Φ) be the subgroup of $\Lambda_1 \cdot \mathrm{Aut}\, R$ (resp. Aut R) leaving $\mathfrak{P}$ fixed. Clearly Φ is the isotropy group of 0 in Ψ. We show that $\Psi \cong \mathrm{Aut}\, \tilde{\Delta}$. Let $\psi\colon X \to \varphi(X) + Y$ belong to Ψ. Then $\psi(0) = Y \in \Lambda_1 \cap \bar{\mathfrak{P}}$, hence $Y = X_k$ with $m_k = 1$. Since $\psi(\mathfrak{P}) = \mathfrak{P}$, it follows from (2) that it can be described by $\alpha_i(\psi(X)) = \alpha_i(\varphi(X)) + \delta_{ik} > 0$, $-\alpha_o(\psi(X)) = -\alpha_o(\varphi(X)) + 1 - \delta_{ok} < 1$. Recalling that φ acts on the dual of V by $\varphi(\alpha)(X) = \alpha(\varphi^{-1}(X))$, this is equivalent with

$$\varphi^{-1}(\alpha_i) > 0 \;,\quad i = 0,\dots,n; i \neq k \;;\quad \varphi^{-1}(\alpha_k) < 1 \;.$$

It follows that $\{\varphi(\alpha_o),\dots,\varphi(\alpha_n)\}$ is a permutation of $\{\alpha_o,\dots,\alpha_n\}$ and φ induces a symmetry of $\tilde{\Delta}$. In this way we obtain a homomorphism f from Ψ into $\mathrm{Aut}\, \tilde{\Delta}$ which is obviously injective. Conversely, let $\varphi \in \mathrm{Aut}\, \tilde{\Delta}$ and $\varphi(\alpha_o) = \alpha_k$. Putting $\psi(X) = \varphi(X) + X_k$, one sees easily that $\psi \in \Psi$ and $f(\psi) = \varphi$. Hence f is an isomorphism. Clearly $f(\Phi)$ is the group of symmetries of Δ, isomorphic with E.

Let Ω be the subgroup of $\Lambda_1 \cdot W$ leaving $\mathfrak{P}$ fixed. Then we get from V, Lemma 2.5, Proposition 2.6 and Theorem 2.9:

$$\Gamma \cdot \Psi = \Lambda_1 \cdot \mathrm{Aut}\ R = \Lambda_1 \cdot W \cdot \Phi = \Gamma \cdot \Omega \cdot \Phi ,$$

and hence $\Psi = \Omega \cdot \Phi \cong Z \cdot E$.

From Table 2, we see now that the only cases where the order of Z does not suffice to determine Z are A_n and D_n . Here Z can be found by a direct computation from the explicit realization as given earlier. From Table 1 and Table 2, we get then the following result, where $\mathbb{D}_n$ is the dihedral group of order $2n$ with generators a,b and relations $a^n = b^2 = 1$, $bab^{-1} = a^{-1}$, and $\mathfrak{S}_n$ denotes the group of permutations of n letters.

R	Z	E	Aut $\tilde{\Delta}$
G_2, F_4, E_8, BC_n	1	1	1
A_1, B_n, C_n, E_7	$\mathbb{Z}_2$	1	$\mathbb{Z}_2$
A_n $(n \geq 2)$	$\mathbb{Z}_{n+1}$	$\mathbb{Z}_2$	$\mathbb{D}_{n+1}$
D_4	$\mathbb{Z}_2 \times \mathbb{Z}_2$	$\mathfrak{S}_3$	$\mathfrak{S}_4$
D_{2n} $(n \geq 3)$	$\mathbb{Z}_2 \times \mathbb{Z}_2$	$\mathbb{Z}_2$	$\mathbb{D}_4$
D_{2n+1} $(n \geq 2)$	$\mathbb{Z}_4$	$\mathbb{Z}_2$	$\mathbb{D}_4$
E_6	$\mathbb{Z}_3$	$\mathbb{Z}_2$	$\mathfrak{S}_3$

Table 3

§2 THE CLASSICAL SPACES

1. The compact classical groups

Let $x=(x_1,\ldots,x_n)\in\mathbb{K}^n$ where $\mathbb{K}=\mathbb{R}$, $\mathbb{C}$ or $\mathbb{H}$. A quadratic matrix $a=(a_{ij})$ with coefficients in $\mathbb{K}$ acts on $\mathbb{K}^n$ by $(ax)_i=\Sigma a_{ik}x_k$. Let $e=I_n$ denote the $n\times n$ unit matrix and put

$$I_{p,q}=\begin{pmatrix}-I_p & 0\\ 0 & I_q\end{pmatrix};\quad J_n=\begin{pmatrix}0 & I_n\\ -I_n & 0\end{pmatrix}.$$

The transpose and (for $\mathbb{K}=\mathbb{C}$) the complex conjugate of a are denoted by ${}^t a$ and $\bar{a}=\tau(a)$. We put $\mathrm{Ad}a.b=aba^{-1}$.

Let $U(n,\mathbb{K})$ denote the group of all matrices leaving the inner product $(x,y)=\Sigma\,\bar{x}_i y_i$ on $\mathbb{K}^n$ invariant. We have $U(n,\mathbb{R})=O(n)$, $U(n,\mathbb{C})=U(n)$, $U(n,\mathbb{H})=Sp(n)$, called the <u>orthogonal</u>, <u>unitary</u>, and <u>symplectic group</u> respectively. $O(n)$ has two connected components, while $U(n)$ and $Sp(n)$ are connected. The orthogonal (resp. unitary) matrices of determinant one are denoted by $SO(n)$ (resp. $SU(n)$). The groups $SU(n)$ and $Sp(n)$ are simply connected for $n\geq 2$ resp. $n\geq 1$. The group $SO(n)$ has a simply connected two-fold covering $Spin(n)$ for $n\geq 3$.

$Sp(n)$ can be realized as a subgroup of $U(2n)$ as follows. Let $e_0=1,e_1,e_2,e_3$ be the usual basis of $\mathbb{H}$ over $\mathbb{R}$.

Then any quaternion q can be written as $q = (a_0 + a_1 e_1) + e_2(a_o + a_1 e_1)$ and $\mathbb{R}1 \oplus \mathbb{R}e_1 \cong \mathbb{C}$. For $z = a_o + \sqrt{-1}\, a_1 \in \mathbb{C}$, we define $qz = q(a_o + a_1 e_1)$. Then $\mathbb{H}$ is a vector space over $\mathbb{C}$ with basis $1, e_2$. Writing $q_i = z_i + e_2 z_{n+i}$, we obtain an isomorphism $\mathbb{H}^n \to \mathbb{C}^{2n}$ of complex vector spaces by $(q_1,\dots,q_n) \to (z_1,\dots,z_{2n})$. For the scalar product, we have $(q,q') = \Sigma \bar{q}_i q_i' = (\Sigma \bar{z}_j z_j') + e_2 \Sigma(z_i z_{n+i}' - z_{n+i} z_i') = (z,z') + e_2 \langle z,z' \rangle$, where $\langle z,z' \rangle$ is a skew-symmetric bilinear form. Under this isomorphism, $Sp(n)$ corresponds to the subgroup of all elements $a \in U(2n)$ such that ${}^t a J_n a = J_n$.

The Lie algebras of $SO(n)$, $SU(n)$, $Sp(n)$ are denoted by $\mathfrak{SO}(n)$, $\mathfrak{SU}(n)$, $\mathfrak{Sp}(n)$. Their root systems are given in Table 1.

2. Classification of involutive automorphisms

1° *Every involutive automorphism of* $SU(n)$ *resp.* $\mathfrak{SU}(n)$ $(n \geq 2)$ *is conjugate to one of the following*:

(A_q^R)	τ (= complex conjugation)	$(n = q+1)$
$(A_{n-1}^{C,q})$	$\mathrm{Ad}\, I_{p,q}$	$(1 \leq q \leq [\frac{n}{2}],\ p+q = n)$
(A_{2q+1}^H)	$\tau \circ \mathrm{Ad}\, J_{q+1}$	$(n = 2(q+1))$

For $n = 2$, τ *is conjugate to* $\mathrm{Ad}\, I_{1,1}$ *and* $\tau \circ \mathrm{Ad}\, J_1 = \mathrm{id}$.

(The meaning of the symbols A_q^R etc. will become clear later.)

Proof. Let $\sigma = \mathrm{Ad}\, g$, where $g \in SU(n)$, be an involutive inner automorphism of $SU(n)$. Then $g^2 = ce$ where $c \in \mathbb{C}$, and putting $a = g/\sqrt{c}$, we see that $\sigma = \mathrm{Ad} a$ where $a^2 = e$ and $a \in U(n)$. Let $V \subset \mathbb{C}^n$ be the fixed point set of a (acting on $\mathbb{C}^n$). Then a is the reflection in V ; hence a is conjugate to $I_{p,q}$ by an element of $U(n)$. If $p < q$, then $I_{p,q}$ is conjugate to $-I_{q,p}$ and since $\mathrm{Ad}(u) = \mathrm{Ad}(-u)$, it follows that σ is conjugate to $\mathrm{Ad} I_{p,q}$, $p \geq q$.

By Table 3, the automorphism group of $SU(n)$ has two connected components for $n \geq 3$. The fixed point set of τ is $SO(n)$ which has rank $[\frac{n+1}{2}] < n$. Hence τ is outer and every other outer automorphism is of the form $\sigma = \tau \circ \mathrm{Ad} g$ with $g \in SU(n)$. Now $\sigma^2 = \mathrm{Ad}\bar{g}g = \mathrm{id}$ implies $\bar{g}g = ce$ with $c \in \mathbb{C}$. Taking transposes, we have $({}^t g)({}^t\bar{g}) = {}^t g g^{-1} = ce$; hence ${}^t g = cg$ and $g = {}^t({}^t g) = c^2 g$; i.e., $c = \pm 1$. In case $c = 1$, g is symmetric, and there is $h \in SO(n)$ such that $f = hgh^{-1}$ is diagonal. Then $\mathrm{Ad} h \circ \sigma \circ \mathrm{Ad} h^{-1} = \tau \circ \mathrm{Ad} f$ and if $f = b^2$, we have $\mathrm{Ad} b \circ \tau \circ \mathrm{Ad} f \circ \mathrm{Ad} b^{-1} = \tau$. In case $c = -1$, g is skew-symmetric, and $n = 2q$ is even. Then there is $h \in SU(n)$ such that $hg{}^t h = J_{q+1}$ and

$$(\mathrm{Ad}\,{}^t h)^{-1} \circ \sigma \circ (\mathrm{Ad}\,{}^t h) = \tau \circ \mathrm{Ad} J_{q+1} .$$

The last assertion follows from the fact that $SU(2)$ has no outer automorphisms or can be verified directly.

2° <u>Every involutive automorphism of</u> $SO(2n+1)$ <u>resp</u>. $\mathfrak{SO}(2n+1)$ $(n \geq 1)$ <u>is conjugate to one of the following</u>:

$$(B_n^{R,q}) \qquad AdI_{p,q} \qquad (1 \leq q \leq n \;,\; p+q = 2n+1)$$

<u>Proof</u>. Since $SO(2n+1)$ has only inner automorphisms and trivial center, $\sigma = Ada$ and $a^2 = e$. Similarly as in case 1°, one sees that σ is conjugate to $AdI_{p,q}$.

3° <u>Every involutive automorphism of</u> $Sp(n)$ <u>resp</u>. $\mathfrak{Sp}(n)$ $(n \geq 1)$ <u>is conjugate to one of the following</u>:

$$(C_q^{R}) \qquad \tau \qquad (n = q)$$
$$(C_n^{H,q}) \qquad AdI_{p,q} \qquad (1 \leq q \leq [\tfrac{n}{2}] \;,\; p+q = n)$$

<u>Proof</u>. $Sp(n)$ has center $\{\pm e\}$ and no outer automorphisms. Let $\sigma = Ada$ be involutive. Then if $a^2 = e$, one sees similarly as before that σ is conjugate to $AdI_{p,q}$. If $a^2 = -e$, we realize $Sp(n)$ as the subgroup $\{u \in U(2n): \tau \circ AdJ_n(u) = u\}$ of $U(2n)$. There exists $b \in Sp(n)$ such that $bab^{-1} = J_n$, and $AdJ_n(u) = \tau(u)$ for $u \in Sp(n)$.

4° <u>Every involutive automorphism of</u> $SO(2n)$ <u>resp</u>. $\mathfrak{SO}(2n)$ $(4 \neq n \geq 1)$ <u>is conjugate to one of the following</u>:

$(D_n^{R,q})$ $\quad \mathrm{AdI}_{p,q}$ $\quad (1 \leq q \leq n\ ,\ p+q=2n)$

(D_n^H) $\quad \mathrm{AdJ}_n$

For $n=1$, $\mathrm{AdJ}_1 = \mathrm{id}$.

Proof. The case $n=1$ is trivial. By Table 3, the automorphism group of $\mathfrak{SO}(2n)$ has two components for $n>4$. Observe that this is still true for $n=2,3$ since the root systems are $A_1 \times A_1$ and A_3 . Let $\rho = \mathrm{AdI}_{2n-1,1}$. Then $SO(2n-1)$ is the connected fixed point set which has rank $n-1$; thus ρ is outer, and $\mathrm{Aut}(SO(2n))$ has two connected components. Hence the automorphisms of $SO(2n)$ (and also of $\mathfrak{SO}(2n)$) are of the form $\sigma = \mathrm{Ad}a$, $a \in O(2n)$. Now $\sigma^2 = \mathrm{id}$ implies $a^2 = \pm e$, and for $a^2 = e$, one sees as before that $\mathrm{Ad}a$ is conjugate to $\mathrm{AdI}_{p,q}$. If $a^2 = -e$, then ${}^t a = -a$ and there is $b \in SO(2n)$ with $bab^{-1} = J_n$.

To treat the case $n=4$, we need an explicit description of the outer automorphisms of order 3 of $\mathfrak{SO}(8)$. We realize $\mathbb{R}^8$ as the underlying vector space of the Cayley division algebra $\mathbb{O}$. Recall that

$$(1) \qquad \mathbb{O} = \mathbb{H} \oplus \mathbb{H}\ell$$

and the multiplication is given by

$$(2) \qquad (x+y\ell)(z+w\ell) = (xz - \bar{w}y) + (wx + y\bar{z})\ell$$

where $x,y,z,w \in \mathbb{H}$. Clearly $\ell^2 = -1$. The scalar product and the involution $^-$ on $\mathbb{O}$ are given by

$$(x + y\ell, z + w\ell) = (x,z) + (y,w) \ ; \quad \overline{x + y\ell} = \bar{x} - y\ell \ . \tag{3}$$

We have

$$\overline{ab} = \bar{b}\bar{a} \ ; \quad a\bar{a} = \bar{a}a = (a,a)1 \tag{4}$$

$$(ab,c) = (b,\bar{a}c) = (a,c\bar{b}) \tag{5}$$

for $a,b,c \in \mathbb{O}$ (the elementary properties of Cayley algebras used here without proof can be found for instance in Schafer [1]). It follows that the trilinear form

$$(a,b,c) = (ab,\bar{c})$$

is invariant under cyclic permutation. A triple (X_1, X_2, X_3) of elements in $\mathfrak{SO}(8)$ will be called a <u>related triple</u> if

$$(X_1(a),b,c) + (a,X_2(b),c) + (a,b,X_3(c)) = 0$$

for all $a,b,c \in \mathbb{O}$. Then clearly a cyclic permutation of a related triple is again a related triple.

LEMMA 2.1. a) (X_1, X_2, X_3) <u>is a related triple if and only if</u>

$$\overline{X_1(\overline{xy})} = X_2(x)y + xX_3(y) \tag{6}$$

<u>for all</u> $x,y \in \mathbb{O}$.

b) <u>The componentwise commutators and linear combinations of related triples are again related triples</u>.

Proof. a) Let (X_1, X_2, X_3) be a related triple. Then for all $x,y,z \in \mathbb{O}$

$$(X_2(x)y, \bar{z}) + (xX_3(y), \bar{z}) + (xy, \overline{X_1(z)}) = 0 .$$

But

$$(xy, \overline{X_1(z)}) = (\overline{xy}, X_1(z)) = -(X_1(\overline{xy}), z) = -(\overline{X_1(\overline{xy})}, \bar{z}) ,$$

and since $(\, , \,)$ is nondegenerate, (6) follows. This argument is reversible.

b) This follows by a straightforward computation using a).

THEOREM 2.2. (Principle of triality) For any $X_1 \in \mathfrak{SO}(8)$, there exist uniquely determined $X_2, X_3 \in \mathfrak{SO}(8)$ such that (X_1, X_2, X_3) is a related triple. The map $\theta\colon X_1 \to X_2$ is an outer automorphism of order 3 of $\mathfrak{SO}(8)$. The group F generated by θ and π where $\pi(X)(a) = \overline{X(\bar{a})}$ is isomorphic with $\mathfrak{S}_3$, and $\mathrm{Aut}\,\mathfrak{SO}(8)$ is the semidirect product $\mathrm{Int}\,\mathfrak{SO}(8) \cdot F$.

Proof. We first prove existence. Every element in $\mathfrak{SO}(8)$ is a sum of transformations of the type $x \to (x,b)a - (x,a)b$ for some $a,b \in \mathbb{O}$, Hence we may assume that X_1 is of this type. Let

$$\begin{aligned} X_1 &: x \to (x,b)a - (x,a)b \\ X_2 &: x \to \tfrac{1}{4}(\bar{a}(bx) - \bar{b}(ax)) \\ X_3 &: x \to \tfrac{1}{4}((xb)\bar{a} - (xa)\bar{b}) \ . \end{aligned} \tag{7}$$

From the alternative law $x(xy) = x^2y$ and (4) follows $\bar{a}(ax) = (\bar{a}a)x = (a,a)x$. Linearizing gives $\bar{a}(bx) + \bar{b}(ax) = 2(a,b)x$ and similarly $(xb)\bar{a} + (xa)\bar{b} = 2(a,b)x$. It follows, using (5),

$$\begin{aligned} 4\overline{X_1(\overline{xy})} &= 4(\overline{xy},b)\bar{a} - 4(\overline{xy},a)\bar{b} = 4(\bar{x},yb)\bar{a} - 4(\bar{y},ax)\bar{b} \\ &= 2x((yb)\bar{a}) - 2(\bar{b}(ax))y \ , \end{aligned}$$

and

$$\begin{aligned} 4X_2(x)y + 4xX_3(y) &= (\bar{a}(bx))y + (\bar{b}(ax))y - x((yb)\bar{a}) \\ &\quad - x((ya)\bar{b}) + 2x((yb)\bar{a}) - 2(\bar{b}(ax))y \\ &= 2(a,b)xy - 2(a,b)xy + 2x((yb)\bar{a}) - 2(\bar{b}(ax))y \ . \end{aligned}$$

For unicity, it suffices to show by Lemma 2.1 b) that $X_1 = 0$ implies $X_2 = X_3 = 0$. If $X_1 = 0$, we have $0 = X_2(x)y + xX_3(y)$. Hence $X_3(y) = -ay$ where $a = X_2(1)$, and it follows $X_2(x) = xa$. Thus $(xa)y - x(ay) = 0$ for all $x,y \in \mathfrak{O}$ which implies that a is a multiple of 1 (see, e.g., Schafer [1]). But $(a,1) = (X_2(1),1) = -(1,X_2(1) = -(1,a)$ shows $a = 0$.

It follows from Lemma 2.1 b) that θ is an automorphism of $\mathfrak{SO}(8)$. Clearly θ is of order 3 and $X_3 = \theta^2(X_1)$. Let $\theta(X) = X$. Then from (6), $\overline{X(1)} = 2X(1)$; hence $X(1) = 0$ and it follows $\overline{X(\bar{x})} = X(x)$. Thus by (6), X is a derivation of $\mathfrak{O}$. Conversely, it is clear that any derivation of $\mathfrak{O}$ is fixed under θ . Since the derivation algebra of $\mathbb{O}$ is $\mathfrak{G}_2$ with rank 2 , θ is outer. Finally, one verifies easily using (7) that $\pi \circ \theta \circ \pi^{-1} = \theta^{-1}$, finishing the proof.

5° Every involutive automorphism of $SO(8)$ resp. $\mathfrak{SO}(8)$ is conjugate to one of the following:

$$\begin{array}{lll} (D_4^{R,q}) & \mathrm{AdI}_{p,q} & (1 \leq q \leq 4 \, , \; p+q=8) \\ (D_4^{H}) & \mathrm{AdJ}_4 & \end{array}$$

The automorphisms $\mathrm{AdI}_{6,2}$ and AdJ_4 of $\mathfrak{SO}(8)$ are conjugate; as automorphisms of $SO(8)$, however, they are not conjugate.

Proof. Since the group E of connected components of $\mathrm{Aut}\,\mathfrak{SO}(8)$ is the symmetric group on three letters, any two elements of order two in E are conjugate. The same reasoning as in 4° shows that every involutive automorphism is conjugate to $\mathrm{AdI}_{p,q}$ or AdJ_4 .

To prove the last statement, write $\mathbb{O} = \mathbb{H} \oplus \mathbb{H}\ell$ as in (1), and let $J(z) = z\ell$ and $T(x+y\ell) = \bar{x} + \bar{y}\ell$ where $z \in \mathbb{O}$, $x,y \in \mathbb{H}$. Then clearly J is conjugate to J_4 and T is conjugate to $I_{6,2}$ (this just amounts to a suitable choice of basis). We will show that

$$\mathrm{AdT} = \theta \circ \mathrm{AdJ} \circ \theta^{-1} \tag{8}$$

where θ is the triality automorphism of Theorem 2.2. Let $X_{a,b}$ be the transformation $x \to (x,b)a - (x,a)b$. It suffices to check that $T\theta(X_{a,b})T = \theta(JX_{a,b}J^{-1})$. We have $JX_{a,b}J^{-1} = X_{Ja,Jb}$. Let $a,b \in \mathbb{H}$. Then we have, using (2), (3), and (4),

$$\begin{aligned} 4T\theta(X_{a,b})T(x+y\ell) &= T(\bar{a}(b(\bar{x}+\bar{y}\ell)) - \bar{b}(a(\bar{x}+\bar{y}\ell))) \\ &= T(\bar{a}b\bar{x} + \bar{y}b\bar{a}\ell - \bar{b}a\bar{x} - \bar{y}a\bar{b}\ell) = x\bar{b}a + a\bar{b}y\ell - x\bar{a}b - b\bar{a}y\ell , \end{aligned}$$

and

$$\begin{aligned} 4\theta(X_{Ja,Jb})(x+y\ell) &= \overline{a\ell}(b\ell(x+y\ell)) - \overline{b\ell}(a\ell(x+y\ell)) \\ &= x\bar{b}a + a\bar{b}y\ell - x\bar{a}b - b\bar{a}y\ell . \end{aligned}$$

A similar computation works for $X_{a,b}$ where $a \in \mathbb{H}$, $b \in \mathbb{H}\ell$, and $a,b \in \mathbb{H}\ell$. This proves (8).

The automorphism θ does not extend to an automorphism of $SO(8)$, since θ permutes the three nontrivial elements in the center of $Spin(8)$ cyclically. Thus $\mathrm{Aut}\, SO(8) = \mathrm{Ad}O(8)$. But a consideration of the eigenvalues of J_4 and $I_{6,2}$ shows that $\mathrm{Ad}J_4$ and $\mathrm{Ad}I_{6,2}$ are not conjugate by an element of $\mathrm{Ad}O(8)$.

3. Determination of the root systems

1° The types $(A_n^{C,q})$, $(B_n^{R,q})$, $(C_n^{H,q})$, $(D_n^{R,q})$ (Grassmann manifolds).

We first consider the automorphisms $\sigma = \mathrm{Ad}I_{p,q}$ of $G = SO(n)$, $SU(n)$, $Sp(n)$, where $p \geq q$ and $p+q = n \geq 2$. Let $e_1, \ldots, e_n$ be the usual basis of $\mathbb{K}^n$ ($\mathbb{K} = \mathbb{R}, \mathbb{C}, \mathbb{H}$). Then $I_{p,q}$ is the reflection in the q-dimensional subspace spanned by $e_{p+1}, \ldots, e_n$, and it follows that G/G^σ can be identified with the Grassmann manifold $M = M(q,n;\mathbb{K})$ of (in the real case nonoriented) q-dimensional subspaces of $\mathbb{K}^n$ (see II, §1). We have $G^\sigma = S(O(p) \times O(q))$, $S(U(p) \times U(q))$, $Sp(p) \times Sp(q)$, imbedded in G as the set of matrices of the form $\left(\begin{array}{c|c} * & 0 \\ \hline 0 & * \end{array}\right)$. Decomposing $\mathfrak{G} = \mathfrak{K} \oplus \mathfrak{M}$ as usual, we have therefore $\mathfrak{K} = \mathfrak{SO}(p) \times \mathfrak{SO}(q)$, $\mathfrak{S}(\mathfrak{U}(p) \times \mathfrak{U}(q)) \cong \mathfrak{SU}(p) \times \mathfrak{SU}(q) \times \mathbb{R}$, $\mathfrak{Sp}(p) \times \mathfrak{Sp}(q)$, and $\mathfrak{M}$ is the set of all skew-hermitian matrices of the form

$$\begin{pmatrix} 0 & \vert & * \\ \hline * & \vert & 0 \end{pmatrix} \quad \begin{matrix} p & q \end{matrix}$$

over $\mathbb{K} = \mathbb{R}, \mathbb{C}, \mathbb{H}$, with Lie triple product $[X,Y,Z] = [[X,Y],Z]$.

Let now E_{ij} denote the matrix having 1 in the i-th row and j-th column and zeros elsewhere. For $r \in \mathbb{K}$, let $X_{ij}(r) = rE_{ij} - \bar{r}E_{ji}$. Here $r \to \bar{r}$ denotes the usual involution in $\mathbb{K}$. We also put $\mathbb{K}_0 = \{r \in \mathbb{K}: \bar{r} + r = 0\}$. Then $X_{ij}(r) \in \mathfrak{G}$, and we have the following formulas:

$$[X_{ij}(r), X_{k\ell}(s)] = 0 \qquad \text{if } \{i,j\} \cap \{k,\ell\} = \emptyset ;$$

$$[X_{ij}(r), X_{jk}(s)] = X_{ik}(rs) \quad \text{if } i \neq k \neq j \neq i ;$$

$$[X_{ij}(r), X_{ji}(s)] = X_{ii}(rs) - X_{jj}(sr) \quad \text{if} \quad i \neq j \ ;$$
$$[X_{ij}(r), X_{jj}(s)] = X_{ij}(rs - r\bar{s}) \quad \text{if} \quad i \neq j \ .$$

Let $H_i = X_{i,p+i}(1)$ and $H = \sum_{i=1}^{q} a_i H_i$ where $a_i \in \mathbb{R}$. Then a computation shows

$$\begin{aligned} &[H, X_{ii}(r) - X_{p+i,p+i}(r)] = -2a_i 2X_{i,p+i}(r) \\ &[H, 2X_{i,p+i}(r)] = 2a_i (X_{ii}(r) - X_{p+i,p+i}(r)) \end{aligned} \tag{9}$$

for $r \in \mathbb{K}_0$ and $1 \leq i \leq q$, and

$$\begin{aligned} &[H, X_{ij}(r) \pm X_{p+i,p+j}(r)] = \pm(a_i \mp a_j)(X_{i,p+j}(r) \mp X_{p+i,j}(r)) \\ &[H, X_{i,p+j}(r) \mp X_{p+i,j}(r)] = \mp(a_i \mp a_j)(X_{ij}(r) \pm X_{p+i,p+j}(r)) \end{aligned} \tag{10}$$

for $r \in \mathbb{K}$ and $1 \leq i < j \leq q$. Here either always the upper or always the lower sign is to be taken. Moreover,

$$\begin{aligned} &[H, X_{ij}(r)] = -a_i X_{p+i,j}(r) \\ &[H, X_{p+i,j}(r)] = a_i X_{ij}(r) \end{aligned} \tag{11}$$

for $r \in \mathbb{K}$, $1 \leq i \leq q$ and $q+1 \leq j \leq p$. Now let $h = \dim_{\mathbb{R}} \mathbb{K} = 1,2,4$ and $\mathfrak{A} = \sum_{i=1}^{q} \mathbb{R} H_i$. Also let λ_i be the linear form on $\mathfrak{A}$ given by $\lambda_i(H) = \frac{1}{\pi} a_i$ $(i = 1, \ldots, q)$. Then it follows from (9), (10), and (11) that $\mathfrak{A}$ is maximal abelian in $\mathfrak{M}$, and we have the root space decomposition

$$\mathfrak{M} = \mathfrak{A} \oplus \Sigma \mathfrak{M}_{\lambda_i} \oplus \Sigma \mathfrak{M}_{2\lambda_i} \oplus \sum_{i<j} \mathfrak{M}_{\lambda_i \pm \lambda_j}$$

where

$$\mathfrak{M}_{\lambda_i} = \sum_{j=q+1}^{p} X_{j,p+i}(\mathbb{K}) \ , \quad m(\lambda_i) = (p-q)h \ ;$$

$$\mathfrak{M}_{2\lambda_i} = X_{i,p+i}(\mathbb{K}_0)\,, \quad m(2\lambda_i) = h-1\,;$$

$$\mathfrak{M}_{\lambda_i \pm \lambda_j} = (X_{i,p+j} \pm X_{p+i,j})(\mathbb{K})\,, \quad m(\lambda_i \pm \lambda_j) = h\,.$$

For the decomposition $\mathfrak{K} = \mathfrak{K}^{\mathfrak{A}} \oplus \Sigma \mathfrak{K}_\lambda$, we get $\mathfrak{K}_{\lambda_i} = \sum_{j=q+1}^{p} X_{ij}(\mathbb{K})$; $\mathfrak{K}_{2\lambda_i} = (X_{ii} - X_{p+i,p+i})(\mathbb{K}_0)$; $\mathfrak{K}_{\lambda_i \pm \lambda_j} = (X_{ij} \mp X_{p+i,p+j})(\mathbb{K})$; and $\mathfrak{K}^{\mathfrak{A}}$ is given as follows:

$\mathbb{K} = \mathbb{R}$: $\mathfrak{K}^{\mathfrak{A}} = \mathfrak{SO}(p-q)$ imbedded in $\mathfrak{SO}(n)$ as the set of matrices of the form

$$\left(\begin{array}{c|c|c} 0 & 0 & 0 \\ \hline 0 & * & 0 \\ \hline 0 & 0 & 0 \end{array}\right)\,.$$
$$\quad q \;\; p$$

$\mathbb{K} = \mathbb{C}$: $\mathfrak{K}^{\mathfrak{A}}$ is the set of matrices of trace 0 in $\Sigma(X_{ii} + X_{p+i,p+i})(\sqrt{-1}\,\mathbb{R}) \oplus \mathfrak{U}(p-q)$, where $\mathfrak{U}(p-q) \subset \mathfrak{U}(n)$ as above. Hence

$$\mathfrak{K}^{\mathfrak{A}} \cong \begin{cases} \mathbb{R}^{q-1} & \\ & \text{for} \\ \mathbb{R}^q \times \mathfrak{SU}(p-q) & \end{cases} \left.\begin{matrix} p = q \\ \\ p > q \end{matrix}\right\}.$$

$\mathbb{K} = \mathbb{H}$: $\mathfrak{K}^{\mathfrak{A}} = \Sigma(X_{ii} + X_{p+i,p+i})(\mathbb{H}_0) \oplus \mathfrak{Sp}(p-q) \cong \mathfrak{SO}(3)^q \times \mathfrak{Sp}(p-q)$.

The inverse roots are $\lambda_i^* = 2\pi H_i$, $(2\lambda_i)^* = \pi H_i$, $(\lambda_i \pm \lambda_j)^* = \pi(H_i \pm H_j)$; hence the root system is B_q, C_q, D_q or BC_q depending on the values of p, q and h. The unit lattice is $\Lambda = \{H \in \mathfrak{A}\colon \exp 2H = e\} = \Sigma\, \mathbb{Z}\pi H_i$. It follows that $\Lambda = \Lambda_0$ for $\mathbb{K} = \mathbb{C}, \mathbb{H}$ and $\Lambda/\Lambda_0 \cong \mathbb{Z}_2$ for $\mathbb{K} = \mathbb{R}$. Hence in the real case the Grassmann manifold $\tilde{M}(q,n;\mathbb{R})$ of oriented subspaces is simply connected. The group of displacements of $\tilde{M}(q,n;\mathbb{R})$ is $SO(n)$ if q or n is odd, and $SO(n)/\{\pm e\}$ if q and n are even. For $M(q,n;\mathbb{C})$ resp. $M(q,n;\mathbb{H})$, it is $SU(n)/\mathbb{Z}_n$ resp. $Sp(n)/\{\pm e\}$ since there σ is inner (see IV, Corollary of Theorem 3.4).

2° The types (A_q^R) and (A_{2q+1}^H).

The fixed point set of τ resp. $\tau \circ \mathrm{Ad}J_{q+1}$ in $SU(n)$ ($n = q+1$ resp. $n = 2(q+1)$) is $SO(n)$ resp. $Sp(q+1)$. For the (-1)-eigenspace $\mathfrak{M}$, we obtain the set of purely imaginary symmetric matrices of trace 0 resp. the set of symplectic symmetric (i.e., $J_q^{-1}\,{}^t a J_q = a$) skew-hermitian matrices.

Let $\mathcal{H}(m,\mathbb{K})$ denote the Jordan algebra of hermitian $m \times m$-matrices over $\mathbb{K} = \mathbb{R}, \mathbb{C}, \mathbb{H}$ and let $\mathcal{H}_0(m,\mathbb{K})$ be the subspace of matrices of trace 0.

LEMMA 2.3. The duals $\mathfrak{M}^* = \sqrt{-1}\,\mathfrak{M}$ are isomorphic to $\mathcal{H}_0(q+1,\mathbb{R})$ in case (A_q^R) and $\mathcal{H}_0(q+1,\mathbb{H})$ in case (A_{2q+1}^H).

Proof. The case (A_q^R) is obvious. Under the usual isomorphism $\mathbb{H}^m \to \mathbb{C}^{2m}$, the elements of $\mathcal{H}_0(m,\mathbb{H})$ correspond to the symplectic symmetric matrices in $\mathcal{H}_0(2m,\mathbb{C})$. Now multiplication with $\sqrt{-1}$ maps hermitian matrices onto skew-hermitian matrices, and our assertion follows.

For $r \in \mathbb{K} = \mathbb{R}, \mathbb{C}, \mathbb{H}$, let $Y_{ik}(r) = rE_{ik} + \bar{r}E_{ki}$. Then $Y_{ik}(r) \in \mathfrak{N}(q+1, \mathbb{K})$, and we have the following formulas:

$$[E_{ii}, Y_{jk}(r)] = 0 \quad \text{for } j \neq i \neq k ;$$

$$[E_{ii}, Y_{ik}(r)] = X_{ik}(r) \quad \text{for } i \neq k ;$$

$$[E_{ii}, X_{jk}(r)] = 0 \quad \text{for } j \neq i \neq k ;$$

$$[E_{ii}, X_{ik}(r)] = Y_{ik}(r) \quad \text{for } i \neq k .$$

Putting $H = \sum_{i=1}^{q+1} a_i \sqrt{-1} E_{ii}$, $a_i \in \mathbb{R}$, we get

$$[H, \sqrt{-1}\, Y_{ik}(r)] = -(a_i - a_k) X_{ik}(r)$$

$$[H, X_{ik}(r)] = (a_i - a_k)\sqrt{-1}\, Y_{ik}(r) .$$

Let $\mathfrak{A} = \{\sum_{i=1}^{q+1} a_i \sqrt{-1}\, E_{ii} : \Sigma a_i = 0\}$ and λ_i the linear form on $\mathfrak{A}$ given by $\lambda_i(H) = a_i/\pi$. Then it follows that $\mathfrak{A}$ is maximal abelian in $\mathfrak{M}$, and we have the root space decomposition $\mathfrak{M} = \mathfrak{A} \oplus \Sigma\, \mathfrak{M}_{\lambda_i - \lambda_j}$ where $\mathfrak{M}_{\lambda_i - \lambda_j} = \sqrt{-1}\, Y_{ij}(\mathbb{K})$, $m(\lambda_i - \lambda_j) = h$. The inverse roots are $(\lambda_i - \lambda_j)^* = \pi\sqrt{-1}(E_{ii} - E_{jj})$ and the root system is A_q. For $\mathfrak{K} = [\mathfrak{M}, \mathfrak{M}]$, we have $\mathfrak{K}_{\lambda_i - \lambda_j} = X_{ij}(\mathbb{K})$ and $\mathfrak{K}^{\mathfrak{A}} = \Sigma\, \mathbb{K}_0 . E_{ii}$; hence $\mathfrak{K}^{\mathfrak{A}} = 0$ for $\mathbb{K} = \mathbb{R}$ and $\mathfrak{K}^{\mathfrak{A}} \cong \mathfrak{SO}(3)^{q+1}$ for $\mathbb{K} = \mathbb{H}$.

The simply connected symmetric space M corresponding to τ (resp. $\tau \circ \mathrm{AdJ}_{q+1}$) can be realized as the component of e of the set of symmetric (resp. symplectic symmetric) unitary matrices of determinant 1. The group of displacements of M is SU(q+1) for q even and SU(q+1)/{±e} for q odd in case (A_q^R), and it is SU(2(q+1))/{±e} in case (A_{2q+1}^H)

3° <u>The type</u> (C_q^R) .

Decomposing an element in $\mathfrak{U}(2n)$ into four blocks, one sees that

$$\mathfrak{Sp}(q) = \left\{ \begin{pmatrix} A & B \\ -\bar{B} & -{}^tA \end{pmatrix} : \begin{array}{ll} A & \text{skew-hermitian} \\ B & \text{complex symmetric} \end{array} \right\} .$$

It follows

$$\mathfrak{K} = \{ \begin{pmatrix} A & B \\ -B & A \end{pmatrix} : A + \sqrt{-1}\, B \in \mathfrak{U}(n) \} \cong \mathfrak{U}(n) ,$$

and since the fixed point set of τ is connected, it is

$$\{ \begin{pmatrix} A & B \\ -B & A \end{pmatrix} : A + \sqrt{-1}\; B \in U(n) \} \cong U(n) .$$

The (-1)-eigenspace is

$$\mathfrak{M} = \{ \sqrt{-1} \begin{pmatrix} A & B \\ B & -A \end{pmatrix} : A, B \text{ real symmetric} \} .$$

The diagonal matrices in $\mathfrak{M}$ form an abelian subspace of dimension n , and since $Sp(n)$ has rank n , it follows that $M = Sp(n)/U(n)$ has rank n . Thus it is a space of maximal rank, the root system is C_n , and all multiplicities are one. Also $\mathfrak{K}^{\mathfrak{A}} = 0$. The group of displacements of M is $Sp(n)/\{\pm e\}$.

4° <u>The type</u> (D_n^H) .

Decomposing an element of $\mathfrak{SO}(2n)$ into four blocks as above, we get

$$\mathfrak{K} = \{ \begin{pmatrix} A & B \\ -B & A \end{pmatrix} : A + iB \in \mathfrak{U}(n) \} \cong \mathfrak{U}(n) ;$$

$$\mathfrak{M} = \{ \begin{pmatrix} A & B \\ B & -A \end{pmatrix} : A, B \in \mathfrak{S}\mathfrak{O}(n) \} .$$

Let $X_{ij} = E_{ij} - E_{ji}$, $q = [\frac{n}{2}]$, and $p = n - q$. Also put $H = \Sigma a_i H_i$, where $H_i = X_{i,p+i} - X_{n+i,n+p+i}$ for $1 \leq i \leq q$. For $1 \leq i < j \leq q$, we put $A^{\pm}_{ij} = X_{i,n+j} \pm X_{j,n+i}$ and

$$B^{\pm}_{ij} = X_{p+i,n+p+j} \pm X_{p+j,n+p+i} ,$$

and for $1 \leq i, j \leq q$:

$$C^{\pm}_{ij} = X_{i,p+n+j} \pm X_{p+j,n+i} .$$

Also for $1 \leq i < j \leq q$ and $\epsilon = \pm 1$ put

$$F^{\pm}_{ij}(\epsilon) = (X_{i,p+j} + \epsilon X_{p+i,j}) \pm (X_{n+i,n+p+j} + \epsilon X_{n+p+i,n+j}) ;$$

$$G^{\pm}_{ij}(\epsilon) = (X_{ij} - \epsilon X_{p+i,p+j}) \pm (X_{n+i,n+j} - \epsilon X_{n+p+i,n+p+j}) .$$

Consider now first the case $n = 2q$, i.e., $p = q$. Then a tedious but straightforward computation shows that we have the root space decomposition

$$\mathfrak{M} = \mathfrak{A} \oplus \sum_{i<j} \mathfrak{M}_{\lambda_i \pm \lambda_j} \oplus \Sigma\, \mathfrak{M}_{2\lambda_i}$$

where $\mathfrak{A} = \sum_{i=1}^{q} \mathbb{R}.H_i$ and $\lambda_i(H) = a_i/\pi$. A basis for $\mathfrak{M}_{\lambda_i \pm \lambda_j}$ is $A^{-}_{ij} \pm B^{-}_{ij}$, $C^{-}_{ij} \pm C^{-}_{ji}$, $F^{-}_{ij}(\epsilon)$, $G^{-}_{ij}(\epsilon)$, and a basis for $\mathfrak{M}_{2\lambda_i}$ is C^{-}_{ii} . Hence $m(\lambda_i \pm \lambda_j) = 4$ and $m(2\lambda_i) = 1$. The inverse roots are $(2\lambda_i)^* = \pi H_i$, $(\lambda_i \pm \lambda_j)^* = \pi(H_i \pm H_j)$. The root system is C_q .

The basis of $\mathfrak{K}_{\lambda_i \pm \lambda_j}$ related to the basis of $\mathfrak{M}_{\lambda_i \pm \lambda_j}$ above is $\pm(C^+_{ij} \mp C^+_{ji})$, $\mp(A^+_{ij} \pm B^+_{ij})$, $\epsilon G^+_{ij}(\epsilon)$, $-\epsilon F^+_{ij}(\epsilon)$. Also $-(X_{i,n+i} + X_{p+i,p+n+i})$ is related to C^-_{ii}. Also let $\mathfrak{L}_i$ be the subspace of $\mathfrak{K}$ spanned by $X_{i,p+i} + X_{n+i,n+p+i}$, $X_{i,n+i} - X_{p+i,n+p+i}$, and $X_{i,n+p+i} + X_{p+i,n+i}$. Then $\mathfrak{L}_i$ is a subalgebra isomorphic with $\mathfrak{SO}(3)$, and $\mathfrak{K}^{\mathfrak{A}} = \Sigma\, \mathfrak{L}_i \cong \mathfrak{SO}(3)^q$. Next consider the case $n = 2q+1$, i.e., $p = q+1$. Then we have the decomposition

$$\mathfrak{M} = \mathfrak{A} \oplus \sum_{i<j} \mathfrak{M}_{\lambda_i \pm \lambda_j} \oplus \Sigma\, \mathfrak{M}_{\lambda_i} \oplus \Sigma\, \mathfrak{M}_{2\lambda_i}$$

where the $\mathfrak{M}_{\lambda_i \pm \lambda_j}$ and $\mathfrak{M}_{2\lambda_i}$ are as above, and a basis for $\mathfrak{M}_{\lambda_i}$ is $X_{i,p} - X_{n+i,n+p}$, $X_{p,p+i} - X_{n+p,n+p+i}$, $X_{i,n+p} - X_{p,n+i}$, $X_{p,n+p+i} - X_{p+i,n+p}$. The related basis of $\mathfrak{K}_\lambda$ is $X_{p,p+i} + X_{n+p,n+p+i}$, $-(X_{i,p} + X_{n+i,n+p})$, $-(X_{p+i,n+p} + X_{p,n+p+i})$, $-(X_{i,n+p} + X_{p,n+i})$. For $\mathfrak{K}^{\mathfrak{A}}$ we have $\Sigma\, \mathfrak{L}_i \oplus \mathbb{R} . X_{p,n+p} \cong \mathfrak{SO}(3)^q \times \mathbb{R}$. The root system is BC_q and the multiplicity of λ_i is 4.

The simply connected symmetric space determined by $\mathrm{Ad} J_n$ can be realized as follows. Let M be the connected component of e of $\{a \in SO(2n) \colon J_n a J_n^{-1} = a^{-1}\}$. Then M is simply connected: for $n = 2q+1$ this follows from the fact that the root system BC_q has trivial center. For $n = 2q$ we have $Z(M) = \{\pm e\}$; indeed, $-e = \exp(\sum_{i=1}^{q} \pi(X_{i,q+i} - X_{n+i,n+q+i})) \in M$. Since the center of the root system C_q is $\mathbb{Z}_2$, M is simply connected. The group of displacements is $SO(2n)/\{\pm e\}$ in either case.

4. Table of classical spaces

The symbols A_q^R, $A_n^{C,q}$, etc. denote the simply connected symmetric spaces M corresponding to the involutive automorphisms as classified earlier. The basic symbol A_q, B_n, etc. denotes the root system of the group of displacements G of M; the subscript is the rank of G. The number q is the rank of M, regardless of its position. The superscript R, C or H indicates that the symmetric space is in some natural way related to $\mathbb{R}$, $\mathbb{C}$, or $\mathbb{H}$. This notation follows the one of Tits [2] for the real forms of simple Lie algebras. É. Cartan's notation (AI, AII, etc.) is also listed.

(Δ, m) is the Dynkin diagram of the root system R of M; the coefficients at the vertices are the multiplicities. In a diagram of type BC_q, the notation ◎ $a[b]$ means that the root α corresponding to the vertex has multiplicity a and 2α has multiplicity b. Note that (Δ, m) determines the multiplicity for any root, since every root is conjugate under the Weyl group to α or 2α where $\alpha \in \Delta$, and the multiplicities are invariant under the Weyl group. Also note that if the symmetric space is related to $\mathbb{K} = \mathbb{R}, \mathbb{C}, \mathbb{H}$ and

	M	R	(Δ,m)	dim M
AI	$A_q^{\mathbb{R}}$ $(q \geq 1)$	A_q	$\overset{1}{\circ}-\overset{1}{\circ}-\dots-\overset{1}{\circ}$	$\frac{(q+1)(q+2)}{2}-1$
AIII	$A_n^{\mathbb{C},q}$ $(1 \leq q < \frac{n+1}{2},\ p+q = n+1 \geq 3)$	BC_q	$\overset{2}{\circ}-\overset{2}{\circ}-\dots-\overset{2}{\circ}\Rightarrow\overset{2(p-q)}{\circledcirc}[1]$	$2pq$
	$A_{2q-1}^{\mathbb{C},q}$ $(q \geq 1)$	C_q	$\overset{2}{\circ}-\overset{2}{\circ}-\dots-\overset{2}{\circ}\Leftarrow\overset{1}{\circ}$	$2q^2$
AII	$A_{2q+1}^{\mathbb{H}}$ $(q \geq 1)$	A_q	$\overset{4}{\circ}-\overset{4}{\circ}-\dots-\overset{4}{\circ}$	$q(2q+3)$
BI	$B_n^{\mathbb{R},q}$ $(1 \leq q \leq n,\ p+q = 2n+1 \geq 3)$	B_q	$\overset{1}{\circ}-\overset{1}{\circ}-\dots-\overset{1}{\circ}\Rightarrow\overset{p-q}{\circ}$	pq
CI	$C_q^{\mathbb{R}}$ $(q \geq 1)$	C_q	$\overset{1}{\circ}-\overset{1}{\circ}-\dots-\overset{1}{\circ}\Leftarrow\overset{1}{\circ}$	$q(q+1)$
CII	$C_n^{\mathbb{H},q}$ $(1 \leq q < \frac{n}{2},\ p+q = n \geq 3)$	BC_q	$\overset{4}{\circ}-\overset{4}{\circ}-\dots-\overset{4}{\circ}\Rightarrow\overset{4(p-q)}{\circledcirc}[3]$	$4pq$
	$C_{2q}^{\mathbb{H},q}$ $(q \geq 1)$	C_q	$\overset{4}{\circ}-\overset{4}{\circ}-\dots-\overset{4}{\circ}\Leftarrow\overset{3}{\circ}$	$4q^2$
DI	$D_n^{\mathbb{R},q}$ $(1 \leq q < n,\ p+q = 2n \geq 4)$	B_q	$\overset{1}{\circ}-\overset{1}{\circ}-\dots-\overset{1}{\circ}\Rightarrow\overset{p-q}{\circ}$	pq
	$D_q^{\mathbb{R},q}$ $(q \geq 2)$	D_q	$\overset{1}{\circ}-\overset{1}{\circ}-\dots-\overset{1}{\circ}<\begin{smallmatrix}\circ^{1}\\ \circ_{1}\end{smallmatrix}$	q^2
DIII	$D_{2q}^{\mathbb{H}}$ $(q \geq 1)$	C_q	$\overset{4}{\circ}-\overset{4}{\circ}-\dots-\overset{4}{\circ}\Leftarrow\overset{1}{\circ}$	$2q(2q-1)$
	$D_{2q+1}^{\mathbb{H}}$ $(q \geq 1)$	BC_q	$\overset{4}{\circ}-\overset{4}{\circ}-\dots-\overset{4}{\circ}\Rightarrow\circledcirc[1]$	$2q(2q+1)$

Table 4

$h = \dim_{\mathbb{R}} \mathbb{K}$, then (Δ,m) contains a subdiagram

$$A_{q-1}\quad \overset{h}{\circ}-\overset{h}{\circ}\dots-\overset{h}{\circ}\ .$$

Finally we remark that the center of M is the group $Z = \Lambda_1/\Lambda_0$ (VI, Corollary of Theorem 3.6) and can therefore be looked up in Table 3.

5. Isomorphisms

Taking into account the isomorphisms among the low-dimensional groups and the isomorphisms $A_1^R \cong A_1^{C,1}$ and $D_4^{R,2} \cong D_4^H$ which were proved in 2, we see that with the following restrictions on the indices, Table 4 is complete and contains no repetitions: A_q^R: $q \geq 2$; $B_n^{R,q}$: $n \geq 2$; C_q^R: $q \geq 3$; $C_n^{H,q}$: $n \geq 3$; $D_n^{R,q}$: $n \geq 4$; D_n^H: $n \geq 5$. It follows now from Table 4 that M is uniquely determined by (Δ, m) . A comparison of the root systems and multiplicities yields the following isomorphisms between the low-dimensional spaces:

$$A_1^{C,1} \cong A_1^R \cong B_1^{R,1} \cong C_1^R \cong D_2^H \cong S^2 \ ;$$

$$B_2^{R,2} \cong C_2^R \ ; \quad B_2^{R,1} \cong C_2^{H,1} \cong S^4 \ ; \quad D_2^{R,1} \cong S^3 \ ;$$

$$D_2^{R,2} \cong S^2 \times S^2 \ ; \quad A_3^R \cong D_3^{R,3} \ ; \quad A_3^{C,2} \cong D_3^{R,2} \ ;$$

$$A_3^H \cong D_3^{R,1} \cong S^5 \ ; \quad A_3^{C,1} \cong D_3^H \cong P_3(\mathbb{C}) \ ;$$

$$D_4^H \cong D_4^{R,2} \ .$$

For the convenience of the reader, we repeat the following isomorphisms, noted before. Here $M(q,n;\mathbb{K})$ is the Grassmann manifold of q-dimensional subspaces of $\mathbb{K}^n$. We have

$P_n(\mathbb{K}) = M(1,n+1;\mathbb{K})$ = projective n-space, and $S^n = \tilde{M}(1,n+1;\mathbb{R})$ = the n-sphere.

$$A_n^{C,q} = M(q,n+1;\mathbb{C}) \ ; \quad B_n^{R,q} = \tilde{M}(q,2n+1;\mathbb{R}) \ ;$$

$$C_n^{H,q} = M(q,n;\mathbb{H}) \ ; \quad D_n^{R,q} = \tilde{M}(q,2n;\mathbb{R}) \ .$$

§3 THE EXCEPTIONAL SPACES

1. Inner automorphisms

Let G be a simple compact Lie group, R its root system relative to a maximal torus T, and $B = \{\alpha_1,\ldots,\alpha_n\}$ a basis of R. Let $-\alpha_0 = \Sigma\, m_i\alpha_i$ be the maximal root (see §1, 4). Then the inequalities

$$\alpha_i > 0 \quad (i = 1,\ldots,n) \ ; \quad -\alpha_0 < 1$$

describe a cell $\mathfrak{P}$ (in this case a simplex) in $\mathfrak{T}$, and we denote by $X_0 = 0$, $X_1,\ldots,X_n$ its vertices, defined by $\alpha_i(X_k) = \frac{1}{m_k}\delta_{ik}$.

THEOREM 3.1. Every inner involutive automorphism σ of G is conjugate to $\mathrm{Ad}\exp X$, where either $X = X_i$ and $m_i = 2$, or $X = \frac{1}{2}X_i$ and $m_i = 1$. Decompose $\mathfrak{G} = \mathfrak{K} \oplus \mathfrak{M}$ relative to σ and let R_a, $(a = 0,1,2)$, be the set of all roots $\alpha = \Sigma\, n_j\alpha_j$ such that $n_i = \pm a$. Then in the first case,

$$\mathfrak{K}_C = \mathfrak{T}_C \oplus \sum_{\alpha \in R_0 \cup R_2} \mathfrak{G}^\alpha \ , \quad \mathfrak{M}_C = \sum_{\alpha \in R_1} \mathfrak{G}^\alpha \ ,$$

$\mathfrak{K}$ is semisimple with root system $R_0 \cup R_2$, and a basis of $R_0 \cup R_2$ is $\{\alpha_0, \ldots, \alpha_{i-1}, \alpha_{i+1}, \ldots, \alpha_n\}$. In the second case,

$$\mathfrak{K}_C = \mathfrak{T}_C \oplus \sum_{\alpha \in R_0} \mathfrak{G}^\alpha \ , \quad \mathfrak{M}_C = \sum_{\alpha \in R_1} \mathfrak{G}^\alpha \ ,$$

the center of $\mathfrak{K}$ is one-dimensional, and a basis for the root system R_0 of $[\mathfrak{K}, \mathfrak{K}]$ is $\{\alpha_1, \ldots, \alpha_{i-1}, \alpha_{i+1}, \ldots, \alpha_n\}$.

Proof. Every element in G is conjugate to an element in $\exp \bar{\mathfrak{P}}$ (V, Corollary of Proposition 3.3). We have to look for $X \in \bar{\mathfrak{P}}$ such that $\operatorname{Ad} \exp X$ is an involutive automorphism of G, i.e., $(\exp X)^2 \in Z(G)$, or $2X \in \Lambda_1$ but $X \notin \Lambda_1$. Recall that $\Lambda_1 = \exp^{-1}(Z(G)) = \{Y \in \mathfrak{T} : \alpha_j(Y) \in \mathbb{Z} \text{ for } j = 1, \ldots, n\}$. Writing $X = \Sigma a_i X_i$ with $a_i \geq 0$, $\Sigma a_i \leq 1$, we get $\frac{2a_i}{m_i} \in \mathbb{Z}$, $i = 1, \ldots, n$. This shows that we have three possibilities:

(1) $$X = X_i \ ; \quad m_i = 2 \ ;$$

(2) $$X = \frac{1}{2} X_i \ ; \quad m_i = 1 \ ;$$

(3) $$X = \frac{1}{2}(X_i + X_j) \ ; \quad m_i = m_j = 1 \ .$$

We show that (3) is conjugate to (2). Since $m_i = 1$, $X_i \in \Lambda_1$. Hence $\mathfrak{P} - X_i$ is another cell (V, Proposition 2.6c)), and since $0 \in \bar{\mathfrak{P}} - X_i$, there exists exactly one w in the Weyl group such that $\mathfrak{P} - X_i = w(\mathfrak{P})$ (V, Theorem 2.9). Thus the transformation $Y \to w^{-1}(Y - X_i)$ leaves $\mathfrak{P}$ fixed and carries X_i into 0. In case (3), X is the midpoint of the segment $\overrightarrow{X_i X_j}$. Hence $w^{-1}(X - X_i)$ is the midpoint of the segment leading from 0 to an X_k with $m_k = 1$; in other words, $w^{-1}(X - X_i) = \frac{1}{2} X_k$. It follows

$$\operatorname{Ad}\exp X = \operatorname{Ad}\exp(X - X_i) = \operatorname{Ad}\exp(w(\tfrac{1}{2}X_k)) = \operatorname{Ad}n \circ \operatorname{Ad}\exp\tfrac{1}{2}X_k \circ \operatorname{Ad}n^{-1} ,$$

where $n \in G$ represents the element $w \in W$.

Let $\alpha \in R_a$ and $E_\alpha \in \mathfrak{G}^\alpha$. Then $\sigma(E_\alpha) = e^{\pi\sqrt{-1}\,a}$, proving the decompositions. The assertion concerning the root systems is clear.

We see that the Dynkin diagram of $\mathfrak{K}$ (resp. $[\mathfrak{K},\mathfrak{K}]$) is obtained from the extended Dynkin Diagram $\tilde{\Delta}$ of $\mathfrak{G}$ as follows:

case (1): delete any vertex with coefficient 2;

case (2): delete α_0 and another vertex with coefficient 1.

From Table 2, we get then the following result (we leave it to the reader to do the same for the classical groups and compare the result with the classification in §2). Here $G_{2(2)}$, $F_{4(-20)}$, etc., denote the simply connected symmetric space, and the subscripts (i) the difference $\dim\mathfrak{M} - \dim\mathfrak{K}$.

M	$\mathfrak{G}$	$\mathfrak{K}$	dim $\mathfrak{M}$	dim $\mathfrak{K}$
$G_{2(2)}$	$\mathfrak{G}_2$	$\mathfrak{A}_1 \times \mathfrak{A}_1$	8	6
$F_{4(-20)}$	$\mathfrak{F}_4$	$\mathfrak{B}_4$	16	36
$F_{4(4)}$		$\mathfrak{A}_1 \times \mathfrak{C}_3$	28	24
$E_{6(-14)}$	$\mathfrak{E}_6$	$\mathfrak{D}_5 \times \mathbb{R}$	32	46
$E_{6(2)}$		$\mathfrak{A}_1 \times \mathfrak{A}_5$	40	38
$E_{7(-25)}$	$\mathfrak{E}_7$	$\mathfrak{E}_6 \times \mathbb{R}$	54	79
$E_{7(-5)}$		$\mathfrak{A}_1 \times \mathfrak{D}_6$	64	69
$E_{7(7)}$		$\mathfrak{A}_7$	70	63
$E_{8(-24)}$	$\mathfrak{E}_8$	$\mathfrak{A}_1 \times \mathfrak{E}_7$	112	136
$E_{8(8)}$		$\mathfrak{D}_8$	128	120

Table 5

In the extended Dynkin diagram of E_6

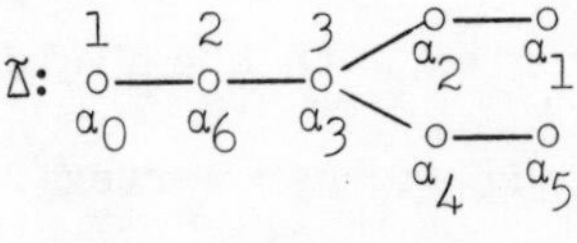

there are three vertices with coefficients 2 . However, since they are conjugate under a symmetry of $\tilde{\Delta}$ and every symmetry of $\tilde{\Delta}$ is induced by an automorphism of R which in turn is induced by an automorphism of $\mathfrak{G}$ (Proposition 1.4 and V, Theorem 4.4), they give rise to conjugate automorphisms. The same remark applies to the vertices with coefficient 1 and also to E_7 . For latter use, we also note that the proof of Theorem 3.1 shows

$$\mathrm{Ad}\,\exp\tfrac{1}{2}X_1 \quad \text{is conjugate to} \quad \mathrm{Ad}\,\exp\tfrac{1}{2}(X_1+X_5)\ , \qquad (4)$$

corresponding to $E_{6(-14)}$.

Finally, the condition for spaces of maximal rank is $\dim \mathfrak{M} - \dim \mathfrak{K} = \operatorname{rank} \mathfrak{G}$ (VI, Proposition 4.1). Hence $G_{2(2)}$, $F_{4(4)}$, $E_{7(7)}$, $E_{8(8)}$ are of maximal rank. The group of displacements is in all cases the centerfree group with Lie algebra $\mathfrak{G}$ (IV, Corollary of Theorem 3.4).

2. Outer automorphisms

PROPOSITION 3.2. *Let G be a compact semisimple Lie group, σ an involutive automorphism of G , and S a maximal torus in the connected fixed point set $(G^\sigma)_0$ of σ . Then S is contained in exactly one maximal torus T of G , and there is a Weyl chamber $\mathfrak{C} \subset \mathfrak{T}$ stable under σ .*

Proof. Let T be a maximal torus in G containing S . We first show $\sigma(T) = T$. For $X \in \mathfrak{T}$, $Y \in \mathfrak{S}$ we have $[X+\sigma(X),Y] = [X,Y] + \sigma[X,Y] = 0$. Hence $X+\sigma(X) \in \mathfrak{S}$ since S is maximal. This proves $\sigma(X) \in \mathfrak{T}$, thus T is stable under σ . Now σ permutes the roots of G relative to T . Assume there is a root α which vanishes on $\mathfrak{S}$. Then $\sigma(\alpha) = -\alpha$. Let $E_\alpha \in \mathfrak{G}^\alpha$; then $\sigma(E_\alpha) = z\bar{E}_\alpha \in \mathfrak{G}^{-\alpha}$, and $E_\alpha = \sigma^2(E_\alpha) = z\overline{\sigma(E_\alpha)} = z\bar{z}E_\alpha$, i.e., $z\bar{z} = 1$. Now $\sigma(E_\alpha + z\bar{E}_\alpha) = E_\alpha + z\bar{E}_\alpha$, and for $X \in \mathfrak{S}$:

$$[X, E_\alpha + z\bar{E}_\alpha] = \alpha(X)(E_\alpha - z\bar{E}_\alpha) = 0 .$$

This contradicts the maximality of $\mathfrak{S}$. Hence no root vanishes on $\mathfrak{S}$. It follows that S contains regular elements of G. Thus T, being the centralizer of S, is uniquely determined. Let $X \in \mathfrak{S}$ such that $\alpha(X) \neq 0$ for all roots. Then X belongs to a Weyl chamber $\mathfrak{C}$ of $\mathfrak{T}$ and $\sigma(X) = X$ implies $\sigma(\mathfrak{C}) = \mathfrak{C}$.

THEOREM 3.3. With the notations of Proposition 3.2, let $\varphi = \sigma \circ \mathrm{Ad}g$ $(g \in G)$ be an involutive automorphism of G. Then φ is conjugate by an inner automorphism to an automorphism of the form $\sigma \circ \mathrm{Ad}y$ where $y \in S$.

Proof. We show first that φ is conjugate to $\sigma \circ \mathrm{Ad}x$ where $x \in T$. Let S' be a maximal torus in $(G^\varphi)_0$ and $S' \subset T'$ as in Proposition 3.2. There is $h \in G$ such that $hT'h^{-1} = T$. Then $\varphi' = \mathrm{Ad}h \circ \varphi \circ \mathrm{Ad}h^{-1}$ leaves T invariant. Let $\mathfrak{C}'$ be a Weyl chamber in $\mathfrak{T}$ invariant under φ' (this exists by Proposition 3.2). There is w in the Weyl group such that $w(\mathfrak{C}') = \mathfrak{C}$. If w is represented by $n \in N(T)$, then $\mathfrak{C}$ is stable under $\varphi'' = \mathrm{Ad}n \circ \varphi' \circ \mathrm{Ad}n^{-1}$. Also $\sigma^{-1} \circ \varphi'' = \mathrm{Ad}x$ is an inner automorphism and $\mathrm{Ad}x$ preserves T and $\mathfrak{C}$. Therefore $x \in N(T)$, and since W is simply transitive on the set of Weyl chambers, $x \in T$. Thus $\varphi'' = \sigma \circ \mathrm{Ad}x$ and φ'' is conjugate to φ by an inner automorphism.

Now let U be the semidirect product of T and $\mathbb{Z}_2 = \{\mathrm{id},\sigma\}$. We denote the pair $(x,\mathrm{id}) \in T \times \mathbb{Z}_2$ by x , and put $(e,\sigma) = s$. Thus $U = T \cup sT$ and $\sigma(x) = sxs^{-1}$ for $x \in T$. Let $\Phi\colon T \times S \to sT$ be defined by $\Phi(x,y) = xsyx^{-1}$. It suffices to show that Φ is surjective. This will be done by showing that Φ is a submersion. Then the image of Φ is open and compact, thus Φ is surjective. Now we have $\Phi(ux,y) = u\Phi(x,y)u^{-1}$ for $u \in T$. Hence it suffices to prove that Φ is surjective on the tangent spaces at the points (e,y) , $y \in S$. Let $(\delta x,\delta y)$ be a tangent vector at (x,y) of $T \times S$. Then

$$\Phi(\delta x,\delta y) = (\delta x)syx^{-1} + xs(\delta y)x^{-1} - xsyx^{-1}(\delta x)x^{-1} ,$$

and for $x = e$, $\delta x = X \in \mathfrak{T}$, and $\delta y = yY$, $Y \in \mathfrak{S}$, we get

$$\Phi(X,yY) = Xsy + syY - syX = sy((sy)^{-1}Xsy - X + Y) = sy(\sigma(X) - X + Y) .$$

Here we use $sy = ys$ and $y^{-1}Xy = X$ since T is abelian. Now X being arbitrary in $\mathfrak{T}$ and $Y \in \mathfrak{S}$, the vectors of the form $\sigma(X) - X + Y$ span $\mathfrak{T}$, and the assertion follows.

PROPOSITION 3.4. *Let* G *be a simply connected compact Lie group with maximal torus* T, *let* B *be a basis for the root system* R *relative to* T, *and let* τ *be an involutive automorphism of* R *leaving* B *invariant (i.e., an automorphism of the Dynkin diagram). Then there exists an involutive automorphism* σ *of* G *extending* τ *and such that* $\sigma|\mathfrak{G}^{\alpha} = \mathrm{id}$ *for all* $\alpha \in B$ *with* $\tau(\alpha) = \alpha$. *Any two such* σ *are conjugate by an inner automorphism of* G. *The restrictions of the roots in* B *to* $\mathfrak{S} = \{X \in \mathfrak{T}\colon \tau(X) = X\}$ *form a basis for the root system of the fixed point set* $K = G^{\sigma}$ *of* σ *relative to the maximal torus* $S = \exp \mathfrak{S}$ *in* K.

Proof. By V, Theorem 4.4, there exists an extension φ of τ to G. Choose $E_{\alpha} \in \mathfrak{G}^{\alpha}$ of length one relative to the positive definite hermitian form $-\beta(\overline{X}, Y)$ of $\mathfrak{G}_C$ where β is the Killing form of $\mathfrak{G}$, for all $\alpha \in B$. Then $\varphi(E_{\alpha}) = z_{\alpha} E_{\tau(\alpha)}$, where $|z_{\alpha}| = 1$. Choose $X \in \mathfrak{T}$ such that $e^{-2\pi\sqrt{-1}\alpha(X)} = z_{\alpha}$ for all $\alpha \in B$. Then we have for $\sigma = \varphi \circ \operatorname{Ad} \exp X$:

$$\sigma(E_{\alpha}) = E_{\tau(\alpha)} \; ; \quad \sigma(\overline{E_{\alpha}}) = \overline{E_{\tau(\alpha)}} \quad \text{for } \alpha \in B .$$

Since $E_{\alpha}, \overline{E_{\alpha}}, \mathfrak{T}$ generate $\mathfrak{G}_C$, it follows that σ is involutive, and $\sigma(E_{\alpha}) = E_{\alpha}$ if $\tau(\alpha) = \alpha$. To show unicity, assume that σ' is also an involutive automorphism of G inducing

τ , and $\sigma'(E_\alpha) = E_\alpha$ if $\tau(\alpha) = \alpha$. Then $\sigma'(E_\alpha) = w_\alpha E_{\tau(\alpha)}$ with $|w_\alpha| = 1$, for $\tau(\alpha) \neq \alpha$, and $\sigma'(E_{\tau(\alpha)}) = \bar{w}_\alpha E_\alpha$ since σ' is involutive. Choose $Y \in \mathfrak{T}$ such that $\alpha(Y) = 0$ if $\tau(\alpha) = \alpha$, and $e^{2\pi\sqrt{-1}(\tau(\alpha)-\alpha)(Y)} = w_\alpha$ if $\tau(\alpha) \neq \alpha$. Then $\mathrm{Ad}\exp Y \circ \sigma \circ \mathrm{Ad}\exp(-Y)$ and σ' coincide on E_α , $\overline{E_\alpha}$, $(\alpha \in B)$, and $\mathfrak{T}$ and are therefore identical.

Since $\tau(B) = B$, we have $\tau(\alpha) \neq -\alpha$ for all $\alpha \in R$; hence no root vanishes on $\mathfrak{S}$. Thus S contains regular elements and T is the only maximal torus of G containing S . Let $S' \supset S$ be a maximal torus in K . Then $S' \subset T$ by Proposition 3.2 and therefore $S' = S$ is a maximal torus in K . We have

$$\mathfrak{K}_C = \mathfrak{S}_C \oplus \Sigma\, \mathfrak{G}^\alpha \oplus \Sigma\, \mathbb{C}(E_\beta + \sigma(E_\beta))$$

where the first sum runs over all $\alpha \in R$ such that $\sigma|\mathfrak{G}^\alpha = \mathrm{id}$, and the second runs over all $\beta \in R$ such that $\sigma(\beta) \neq \beta$. Hence the roots of K with respect to S are restrictions of certain roots in R to $\mathfrak{S}$. In particular, the restrictions of all $\alpha \in B$ occur. Since every root in R is an integer linear combination of roots in B with coefficients of the same sign, every root of K is such a linear combination of roots in $B|\mathfrak{S}$.

We call σ the <u>normal extension</u> of τ . Now we can apply these results to classify the involutive outer automorphisms of the exceptional groups. By Table 3, only the groups of type E_6 have nontrivial outer automorphisms. Thus let $G = \underline{\underline{E}}_6$ and let σ be the normal extension of

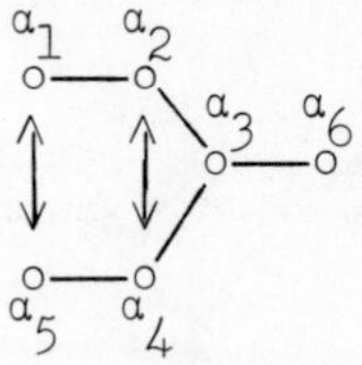

Let $H_i = \vec{\alpha}_i$. Then $\mathfrak{S}$ is spanned by $\frac{1}{2}(H_1 + H_5)$, $\frac{1}{2}(H_2 + H_4)$, H_3 , H_6 , and an easy calculation shows that the Dynkin diagram of $B|\mathfrak{S}$ is

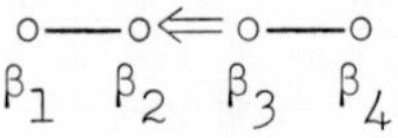

where $\beta_1 = \alpha_1|\mathfrak{S} = \alpha_5|\mathfrak{S}$; $\beta_2 = \alpha_2|\mathfrak{S} = \alpha_4|\mathfrak{S}$; $\beta_3 = \alpha_3|\mathfrak{S}$ and $\beta_4 = \alpha_4|\mathfrak{S}$. Hence $K = \underline{\underline{F}}_4$. A cell $\mathfrak{P}$ in $\mathfrak{S}$ is described by the inequalities

$$\beta_i > 0 \ , \quad i = 1,\dots,4 \ ; \quad 2\beta_1 + 4\beta_2 + 3\beta_3 + 2\beta_4 < 1 \ .$$

Let $X_0 = 0$, $X_1,\dots,X_4$ be the vertices of $\mathfrak{P}$. By Theorem 3.3, every other outer involutive automorphism of G is of the form $\varphi = \sigma \circ \mathrm{Ad}\, y$, where $y \in S$. Now any $y \in S$ is in K conjugate to some $\exp X$ with $X \in \overline{\mathfrak{P}}$, hence $\sigma \circ \mathrm{Ad}\, y$ is conjugate to $\sigma \circ \mathrm{Ad} \exp X$. Moreover, since $\sigma(X) = X$, the automorphism $\sigma \circ \mathrm{Ad} \exp X$ will be involutive iff $\mathrm{Ad}(\exp X)^2 = \mathrm{id}$ iff $2X \in \Lambda_1(K)$. By Theorem 3.1, this leaves the two possibilities $X = X_1$ and $X = X_4$.

We shall show that $\sigma \circ \mathrm{Ad}\exp X_1$ is conjugate to σ. Let $H_1', \dots, H_6'$ be the basis of $\mathfrak{T}$ dual to $\alpha_1, \dots, \alpha_6$, i.e., $\alpha_i(H_k') = \delta_{ik}$. Then $\Lambda_1(G) = \Sigma\, \mathbb{Z} H_i'$. Let $Z = H_1' + H_2' - H_4' \in \Lambda_1(G)$. Then the component in $\mathfrak{S}$ of Z is X_1, i.e., $Z = X_1 + Y$, where $\sigma(Y) = -Y$. Indeed, the (-1)-eigenspace of σ is given by $\alpha_1 + \alpha_5 = 0$ and $\alpha_2 + \alpha_4 = 0$, and we have

$$(\alpha_1 + \alpha_5)(Z - X_1) = \alpha_1(H_1') - \alpha_1(X_1) - \alpha_5(X_1) = 1 - 2\beta_1(X_1) = 0$$

and

$$(\alpha_2 + \alpha_4)(Z - X_1) = \alpha_2(H_2') - \alpha_4(H_4') - 2\beta_2(X_1) = 0 .$$

It follows

$$\begin{aligned} &\mathrm{Ad}\exp(-\tfrac{Y}{2}) \circ (\sigma \circ \mathrm{Ad}\exp X_1) \circ \mathrm{Ad}\exp(\tfrac{Y}{2}) = \\ &\quad = \sigma \circ \mathrm{Ad}\exp\tfrac{Y}{2} \circ \mathrm{Ad}\exp X_1 \circ \mathrm{Ad}\exp\tfrac{Y}{2} = \sigma \circ \mathrm{Ad}\exp(X_1 + Y) \\ &\quad = \sigma \circ \mathrm{Ad}\exp Z = \sigma . \end{aligned}$$

The symmetric space G/K corresponding to σ has dimension $78 - 52 = 26$; hence it is not of maximal rank. By the remark at the end of $\underline{\underline{1}}$, the space of maximal rank corresponding to E_6 is still missing, and must therefore be given by $\tau = \sigma \circ \mathrm{Ad}\exp X_4$. By VI, Proposition 4.1, it has dimension $\frac{1}{2}(78 + 6) = 42$. The fixed point set $\mathfrak{H}$ of τ in $\mathfrak{G} = \mathfrak{E}_6$ has rank 4 and dimension 36; it is therefore $\mathfrak{B}_4$ of $\mathfrak{C}_4$. By the results of $\underline{\underline{1}}$, $\varphi = \mathrm{Ad}\exp X_4$ is an involutive automorphism of $K = \underline{\underline{F}}_4$ with fixed point set $\mathfrak{A}_1 \times \mathfrak{C}_3$ in $\mathfrak{K}$. Also, φ

induces an involutive automorphism of $\mathfrak{H}$ since $\sigma\circ\varphi=\varphi\circ\sigma = \tau$, and the fixed point set of φ in $\mathfrak{H}$ is $\mathfrak{A}_1\times\mathfrak{C}_3$. Checking now the list of symmetric spaces of classical type, we see that $\mathfrak{B}_4=\mathfrak{SO}(9)$ does not have involutive automorphisms with fixed point set $\mathfrak{A}_1\times\mathfrak{C}_3$. It follows that $\mathfrak{H}=\mathfrak{C}_4$.

M	$\mathfrak{G}$	$\mathfrak{K}$	dim $\mathfrak{M}$	dim $\mathfrak{K}$
$E_{6(-26)}$	$\mathfrak{E}_6$	$\mathfrak{F}_4$	26	52
$E_{6(6)}$		$\mathfrak{C}_4$	42	36

Table 6

Note that the group of displacements in these two cases is the simply connected group $\underline{\underline{E}}_6$, since the outer automorphisms act nontrivially on the center $\mathbb{Z}_3$ (see IV, Corollary of Theorem 3.4).

$\underline{\underline{3}}$. Satake diagrams

Let M be a compact semisimple symmetric space, G its group of displacements, K the isotropy group of the base point, A a maximal torus in M, $T\supset Q(A)$ a maximal torus in G. Let R be the root system of G relative to T and R_- the root system of M relative to A. For $\alpha\in R$ let $\bar{\alpha}=2\alpha|\mathfrak{A}=\alpha-\sigma(\alpha)$. Then $R_-=\{\bar{\alpha}\colon\ \bar{\alpha}\neq 0, \alpha\in R\}$ (see VI,

Proposition 3.3). Also let $R_0 = \{\alpha \in R\colon \bar{\alpha} = 0\}$. Let $\mathfrak{C}_-$ be a Weyl chamber in $\mathfrak{A}$ and $\mathfrak{C}$ a Weyl chamber in $\mathfrak{T}$ such that $\bar{\mathfrak{C}}_- \subset \bar{\mathfrak{C}}$. Let B_- (resp. B) denote the basis of R_- (resp. R) corresponding to $\mathfrak{C}_-$ (resp. $\mathfrak{C}$).

LEMMA 3.5. $B_0 = B \cap R_0$ _is a basis for_ R_0.

Proof. Let $\beta = \sum_{\alpha \in B} n_\alpha \alpha \in R_0$. Then $0 = \beta(X) = \sum n_\alpha \alpha(X)$ for all $X \in \mathfrak{C}_-$, and $\alpha(X) \geq 0$. Hence $n_\alpha \neq 0$ implies $\alpha(X) = 0$, i.e., $\alpha \in B_0$. It follows that B_0 is a basis for R_0.

PROPOSITION 3.6. _Let_ $B \setminus B_0 = \{\alpha_1, \ldots, \alpha_r\}$ _and_ $B_0 = \{\beta_1, \ldots, \beta_s\}$. _Then_

$$-\sigma(\alpha_i) = \alpha_{\pi(i)} + \sum n_{i\ell} \beta_\ell \tag{5}$$

where π _is an involutive permutation of_ $\{1, \ldots, r\}$ _and the_ $n_{i\ell}$ _are non-negative integers. We have_ $B_- = \{\bar{\alpha}\colon \alpha \in B \setminus B_0\}$, _and the rank of_ M _equals the number of cycles of_ π.

Proof. Let α be a positive root in R, i.e., α takes positive values on $\mathfrak{C}$, and let $\bar{\alpha} \neq 0$. Then $-\overline{\sigma(\alpha)} = \bar{\alpha}$ shows that $-\sigma(\alpha)$ is positive on $\mathfrak{C}_-$ and therefore also on $\mathfrak{C}$. It follows for $\alpha = \alpha_i$

$$-\sigma(\alpha_i) = \sum m_{ij} \alpha_j + \sum n_{i\ell} \beta_\ell ,$$

where m_{ij}, $n_{i\ell}$ are non-negative integers and

$$\alpha_i = (-\sigma)^2(\alpha_i) = \Sigma\, m_{ij} m_{jk} \alpha_k + \Sigma(m_{ij} n_{j\ell} - n_{i\ell})\beta_\ell \,.$$

Hence $\Sigma\, m_{ij} m_{jk} = \delta_{ik}$, and since the m_{ij} are non-negative integers, the matrix (m_{ij}) is a permutation matrix. This proves (5).

Clearly every root in R_- is an integer linear combination with coefficients of the same sign of roots $\bar{\alpha}$, $\alpha \in B \setminus B_0$. It remains to show that these are linearly independent. Let $\alpha_i, \alpha_j \in B \setminus B_0$ and $\bar{\alpha}_i \neq \bar{\alpha}_j$. Then

$$\begin{aligned}(\bar{\alpha}_i, \bar{\alpha}_j) &= (\alpha_i - \sigma(\alpha_i), \alpha_j - \sigma(\alpha_j)) = 2((\alpha_i, \alpha_j) + (\alpha_i, -\sigma(\alpha_j)))\\ &= 2((\alpha_i, \alpha_j) + (\alpha_i, \alpha_{\pi(j)}) + \Sigma\, n_{j\ell}(\alpha_i, \beta_\ell)) \leq 0\end{aligned}$$

by V, 2° in the proof of Theorem 2.2, and since $i \neq \pi(j)$. By V, Lemma 2.3, $\{\bar{\alpha}\colon \alpha \in B \setminus B_0\}$ is linearly independent.

The last assertion follows now from the fact that $\bar{\alpha}_i = \bar{\alpha}_k$ iff $k = i$ or $k = \pi(i)$. Indeed, $\bar{\alpha}_i = \bar{\alpha}_k$ implies

$$\alpha_i + \alpha_{\pi(i)} + \Sigma\, n_{i\ell}\beta_\ell = \alpha_k + \alpha_{\pi(k)} + \Sigma\, n_{k\ell}\beta_\ell \,,$$

and the converse is trivial.

We now associate with B its <u>Satake diagram</u> Σ as follows. In the Dynkin diagram of B, denote the roots α_i by $\circ$ as usual ("white roots") and the roots β_ℓ by $\bullet$ ("black roots"). If $\pi(i) = k$, indicate this by $\circ \overset{\curvearrowleft\!\curvearrowright}{} \circ$. From Σ we can read off the following information.

(i) π ;

(ii) rank M (= number of cycles of π);

(iii) rank $\mathfrak{K}^{\mathfrak{A}} = \text{rank } G - \text{rank } M$ (see VI, Proposition 3.3 d));

(iv) the root system of $\mathfrak{K}^{\mathfrak{A}}$ (the black roots are the Dynkin diagram of $\mathfrak{K}^{\mathfrak{A}}$, by Lemma 3.5 and VI, Proposition 3.3 d));

(v) dim $\mathfrak{K}^{\mathfrak{A}}$ (by (iii) and (iv));

(vi) $\dim M = \frac{1}{2}(\dim G - \dim \mathfrak{K}^{\mathfrak{A}} + \text{rank } M)$ (see VI, Proposition 1.4).

LEMMA 3.7. <u>The Satake diagram determines the involution</u> σ <u>of</u> R <u>uniquely</u>.

<u>Proof</u>. It suffices to know the effect of σ on B . We have $\sigma(\beta_i) = \beta_i$. Since Σ determines π , we have to compute the coefficients $n_{i\ell}$ in (5) of Proposition 3.6. From (5) we get

$$\begin{aligned}\Sigma\, n_{i\ell}\beta_\ell(\beta_k^*) &= -\sigma(\alpha_i)(\beta_k^*) - \alpha_{\pi(i)}(\beta_k^*) \\ &= -\alpha_i(\beta_k^*) - \alpha_{\pi(i)}(\beta_k^*)\ .\end{aligned}$$

Since the numbers $\alpha(\beta^*)$ $(\alpha, \beta \in B)$ are determined by the Dynkin diagram of B , and since the matrix $(\beta_\ell(\beta_k^*))$ is nondegenerate, we can solve for $n_{i\ell}$.

Let $\lambda \in B_-$, and let Σ_λ be the subdiagram of Σ obtained as follows. Erase all white roots α such that $\bar{\alpha} \neq \lambda$, then erase all black roots not connected by a chain to one of the remaining white roots (clearly at most two white roots can remain). Let R_λ be the set of roots in R which are linear combinations of roots in Σ_λ. Let $\mathfrak{T}_\lambda$ be the subspace of $\mathfrak{T}$ spanned by α^*, $\alpha \in R_\lambda$. Then R_λ is a root system for $\mathfrak{T}_\lambda$ and Σ_λ is a basis for R_λ.

LEMMA 3.8. R_λ <u>contains all roots</u> $\gamma \in R$ <u>such that</u> $\bar{\gamma}$ <u>is a nonzero multiple of</u> λ. <u>It is stable under</u> σ.

<u>Proof</u>. Let $\gamma = \Sigma\, m_i \alpha_i + \Sigma\, n_\ell \beta_\ell \in R$ and $\bar{\gamma} = c\lambda$. Then by Proposition 3.6, $m_i = 0$ if $\bar{\alpha}_i \neq \lambda$. Now $B' = \{\alpha \in B\colon \bar{\alpha} = 0$ or $\bar{\alpha} = \lambda\}$ decomposes into several indecomposable components, and every root which is a linear combination of elements in B' is a linear combination of elements in one component (V, Proposition 4.1). It follows that γ is a linear combination of elements in Σ_λ.

Now let $\beta \in R_\lambda$. If $\bar{\beta} = 0$, then $\sigma(\beta) = \beta$. If $\bar{\beta} = c\lambda$, then $\overline{\sigma(\beta)} = -c\lambda$, therefore $\sigma(\beta) \in R_\lambda$.

For any $\lambda \in B_-$, let now $\mathfrak{G}(\lambda)$ be the subalgebra of $\mathfrak{G}$ corresponding to R_λ, i.e.,

$$\mathfrak{G}(\lambda) = \mathfrak{T}_\lambda \oplus (\mathfrak{G} \cap \sum_{\alpha \in R_\lambda} \mathfrak{G}^\alpha) .$$

Clearly $\mathfrak{G}(\lambda)$ is a compact Lie algebra, $\mathfrak{T}_\lambda$ is a maximal abelian subalgebra and R_λ is the corresponding root system. It is also stable under σ , and we have

$$\mathfrak{M}(\lambda) = \mathfrak{G}(\lambda) \cap \mathfrak{M} = \mathbb{R}.\vec{\lambda} \oplus \sum_{0 \neq c \in \mathbb{R}} \mathfrak{M}_{c\lambda} .$$

The symmetric subspace of M corresponding to $\mathfrak{M}(\lambda)$ is a symmetric space of rank one, and its Satake diagram is Σ_λ . The significance of this is the following: if we know the Satake diagrams of spaces of rank one, we know all the possibilities for Σ_λ , which restricts the possibilities for Σ considerably.

From our results in §2, we see that the spaces of rank one of classical type are the spheres S^n , $n \geq 2$, and the projective spaces $P^n(\mathbb{K})$, $\mathbb{K} = \mathbb{R}, \mathbb{C}, \mathbb{H}$, $n \geq 2$. The list of their Satake diagrams is

M	Σ	σ
$S^2 = A_1^R$	o α_1	$-\sigma(\alpha_1) = \alpha_1$
S^3	α_1 o ↔ o α_2	$-\sigma(\alpha_1) = \alpha_2$
$S^5 = A_3^H$	α_1 α_2 α_3: •—o—•	$-\sigma(\alpha_2) = \alpha_1 + \alpha_2 + \alpha_3$
$S^{2n} = B_n^{R,1}$	α_1 α_2 … α_n: o—•—. . .—•⇒•	$-\sigma(\alpha_1) = \alpha_1 + 2\sum_{i=2}^{n}\alpha_i$
$S^{2n-1} = D_n^{R,1}$	α_1 α_2 … α_{n-1}, α_n: o—•—. . .—•< (• α_{n-1}, • α_n)	$-\sigma(\alpha_1) = \alpha_1 + 2\sum_{i=2}^{n-2}\alpha_i + \alpha_{n-1} + \alpha_n$
$P_n(\mathbb{C}) = A_n^{C,1}$	o—•—. . .—•—o (α_1 ↔ α_n), α_1 α_2 … α_n	$-\sigma(\alpha_1) = \sum_{i=2}^{n}\alpha_i$
$P_{n-1}(\mathbb{H}) = C_n^{H,1}$	α_1 α_2 α_3 … α_n: •—o—•—. . .—•⇐•	$-\sigma(\alpha_2) = \alpha_1 + \alpha_2 + 2\sum_{i=3}^{n-1}\alpha_i + \alpha_n$

Table 7

The Satake diagrams follow immediately from the structure of $\mathfrak{R}^{\mathfrak{A}}$ determined in §2, except for $P_n(\mathbb{C})$, where

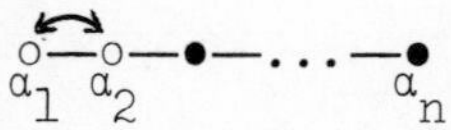

would be possible. This would imply

$$-\sigma(\alpha_1) = \alpha_2 + \sum_3^n m_i \alpha_i ,$$

and for $k > 2$:

$$0 = (-\sigma(\alpha_1), \alpha_k) = 2m_k - m_{k-1} - m_{k+1} ,$$

where $m_2 = 1$.

For $k = n$, we have $2m_n = m_{n-1}$. Hence $m_n = m_{n-1} = 0$, because the highest root is $\alpha_1 + \ldots + \alpha_n$. This implies $m_2 = 0$, a contradiction. The formulas for σ are computed by the method of Lemma 3.7.

4. Determination of the root systems

We first remark that for a space of maximal rank $\mathfrak{A} = \mathfrak{T}$ and $\sigma = -\mathrm{id}$. Hence there are only white roots and the permutation π is the identity. Therefore the Satake diagram is just the ordinary Dynkin diagram. Also $R_- = 2R$ and all multiplicities are one (VI, Proposition 4.1). This takes care of the spaces $G_{2(2)}$, $F_{4(4)}$, $E_{6(6)}$, $E_{7(7)}$, and $E_{8(8)}$.

To find the other diagrams, we proceed as follows. First the diagrams leading to spaces of rank one are determined. This gives us, together with Table 7, a list of all possible subdiagrams Σ_λ . If Σ is a candidate having only admissible subdiagrams Σ_λ , we compute the dimension of the corresponding space by (vi). Since we know the possible dimensions already (Tables 5 and 6), this gives a criterion for whether Σ is possible or not. If this does not suffice, we can (by Lemma 3.7) compute σ explicitly from Σ and use further properties of σ .

<u>Satake diagrams of type</u> F_4

Dynkin diagram: $\overset{\alpha_1}{\circ}-\overset{\alpha_2}{\circ}\Leftarrow\overset{\alpha_3}{\circ}-\overset{\alpha_4}{\circ}$.

Maximal root: $\omega = 2\alpha_1 + 3\alpha_2 + 4\alpha_3 + 2\alpha_4$.

We first look for Satake diagrams corresponding to a symmetric space of rank one. In that case, $B_- = \{\lambda\}$, and if α_i is a white root, then $\bar{\alpha}_i = \lambda$ by Proposition 3.6. Now $R_- = \{\pm\lambda\}$ or $R_- = \{\pm\lambda, \pm 2\lambda\}$, and since $\bar{\omega} \in R_-$, we have only two possibilities:

(a) $\circ - \bullet \Leftarrow \bullet - \bullet$,

(b) $\bullet - \bullet \Leftarrow \bullet - \circ$.

A computation using Lemma 4.3 shows

(a) $-\sigma(\alpha_1) = \alpha_1 + 3\alpha_2 + 2\alpha_3 + \alpha_4$,

(b) $-\sigma(\alpha_4) = 2\alpha_1 + 4\alpha_2 + 3\alpha_3 + \alpha_4$.

Consulting a table of roots of F_4 (e.g., Tits [2]), we see that in case (b) $\alpha = 2\alpha_1 + 3\alpha_2 + 2\alpha_3 + \alpha_4 \in R$ and also $\alpha + \sigma(\alpha) = 2\alpha_1 + 2\alpha_2 + \alpha_3 \in R$, which is impossible by VI, Proposition

3.3. Thus (b) is ruled out.

We show now that (a) actually is the Satake diagram of $F_{4(-20)}$ by showing that it is the only one possible. Thus let Σ be a Satake diagram of type F_4, assume that α_1 is white and we are not in case (a). Then $\Sigma_{\bar{\alpha}_1}$ is of classical type, and by Table 7, there are the two possibilities $\underset{\alpha_1}{\circ}$ and and $\overset{\leftrightarrow}{\underset{\alpha_1}{\circ}\!-\!\underset{\alpha_2}{\circ}}$. In either case, α_2 is white. Then also α_3 is white, or else $\Sigma_{\bar{\alpha}_2}$ would contain a figure $\circ\Leftarrow\bullet$ which is impossible by Table 7. Finally, the assumption α_4 black leads to $\Sigma_{\bar{\alpha}_3} = \circ\!-\!\bullet$, which is impossible by Table 7. This leaves the following four possibilities for Σ :

$$\circ\!-\!\circ\Leftarrow\circ\!-\!\circ\ ,\quad \overset{\leftrightarrow}{\circ\!-\!\circ}\Leftarrow\circ\!-\!\circ\ ,\quad \circ\!-\!\circ\Leftarrow\overset{\leftrightarrow}{\circ\!-\!\circ}\ ,\quad \overset{\leftrightarrow}{\circ\!-\!\circ}\Leftarrow\overset{\leftrightarrow}{\circ\!-\!\circ}\ .$$

Computing the dimensions of the corresponding spaces (see (vi)), we get 28 , 27 , 27 , 26 . Hence by Table 5 only the first one is possible, and it corresponds to $F_{4(4)}$ as we know.

Now assume that α_1 is black. Then by Table 7, Σ_λ containing α_1 must be $\underset{}{\overset{\alpha_1}{\bullet}}\!-\!\overset{\alpha_2}{\circ}\Leftarrow\overset{\alpha_3}{\bullet}$. Hence α_4 is white which would give $\Sigma_{\bar{\alpha}_4} = \bullet\!-\!\circ$, a contradiction.

Now for $F_{4(-20)}$, $\Sigma = \circ\!-\!\bullet\Leftarrow\bullet\!-\!\bullet$, let $\lambda = \bar{\alpha}_1$. Then $R_- = \{\pm\lambda, \pm 2\lambda\}$, and a glance at the list of roots of F_4 shows $m(\lambda) = 8$, $m(2\lambda) = 7$.

<u>Satake diagrams of type</u> E_6

Dynkin diagram: 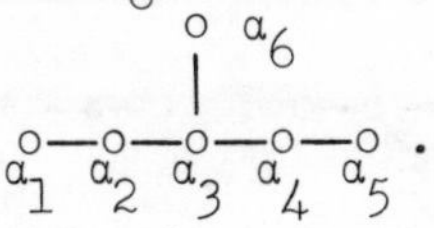

Maximal root: $\omega = \alpha_1 + 2\alpha_2 + 3\alpha_3 + 2\alpha_4 + \alpha_5 + 2\alpha_6$.

A similar consideration as in case F_4 shows that the only possibilities for diagrams of spaces of rank one are

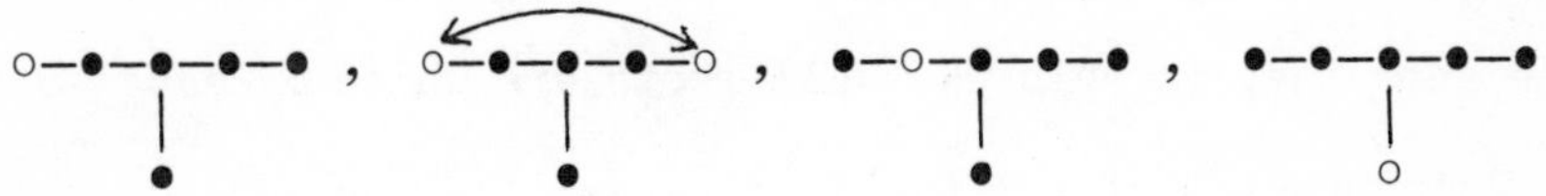

leading to dimensions 17 , 25 , 26 , 44 . In the third case, $\mathfrak{K}^{\mathfrak{A}} = \mathfrak{A}_1 \times \mathfrak{A}_4$ has rank five, but the only space of dimension 26 is $E_{6(-26)}$ and there $\mathfrak{K} = \mathfrak{F}_4$, of rank four. Hence there are no spaces of rank one. Thus we get from Table 7 the following list of possibilities for Σ_λ .

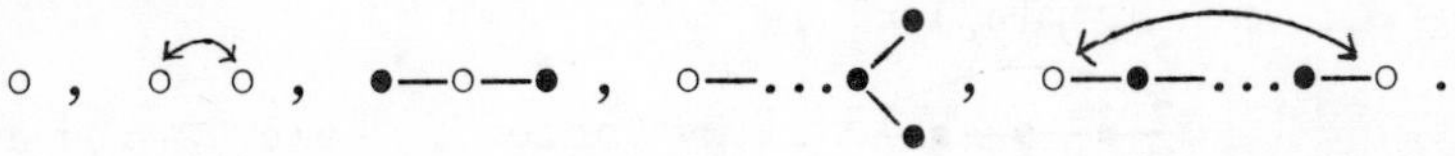

Assume α_1 black. Then Σ_λ containing α_1 must be ●—o—● , and this leads to

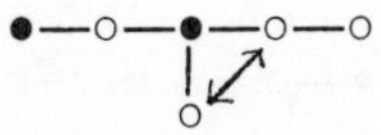

of dimension 37, which does not occur. Thus α_1 is white and similarly α_5 is white.

Assume α_2 black. Then $\Sigma_{\alpha_1}^-$ is 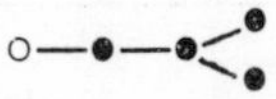 or  . In the first case, we obtain 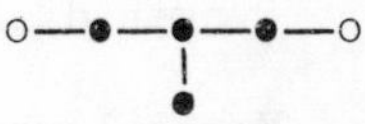

of dimension 26 . In the second case, we get

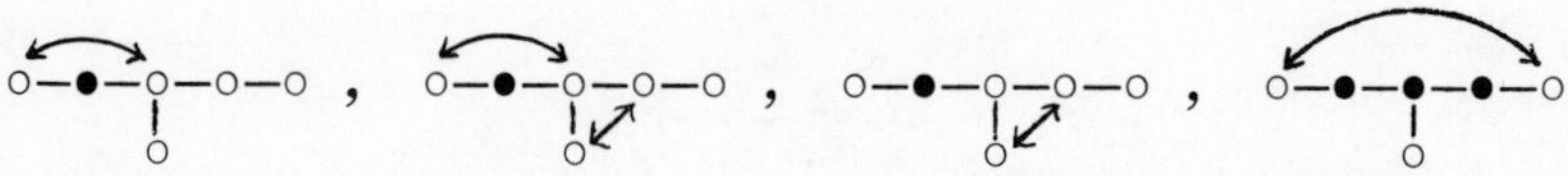

with dimensions 39 , 38 , 38 , 32. Thus only the last one is possible.

Assume α_2 white. Checking all possibilities for Σ_λ , one sees that in this case all roots are white . Hence $-\sigma$ is an automorphism of the Dynkin diagram. If $-\sigma$ is not the identity, we must have 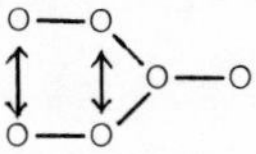 of dimension 40 . Altogether, we have the following result.

$E_{6(2)}$ 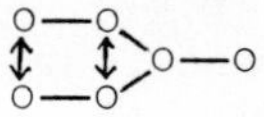 . The rank of M is 4 , and one computes that the Dynkin diagram of B_- is 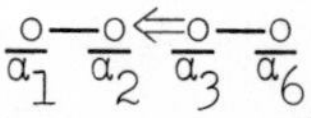 . The table of roots for E_6 yields the multiplicities $m(\bar{\alpha}_1) = m(\bar{\alpha}_2) = 2$, $m(\bar{\alpha}_3) = m(\bar{\alpha}_6) = 1$.

$E_{6(-14)}$ 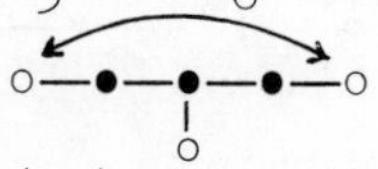 . By Table 7, $-\sigma(\alpha_1) = \alpha_2 + \alpha_3 + \alpha_4 + \alpha_5$, $-\sigma(\alpha_6) = \alpha_2 + 2\alpha_3 + \alpha_4 + \alpha_6$. For B_- one gets

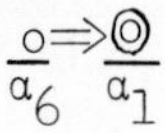 , $m(\bar{\alpha}_6) = 6$, $m(\bar{\alpha}_1) = 8$, $m(2\bar{\alpha}_1) = 1$.

$E_{6(-26)}$ 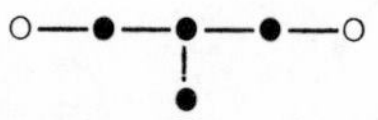 . Here $\bar{\alpha}_1$ and $\bar{\alpha}_5$ have the same length, hence B_- is 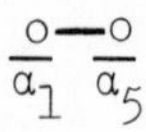 and $m(\bar{\alpha}_1) = m(\bar{\alpha}_5) = 8$.

<u>Satake diagrams of type</u> E_7

Dynkin diagram: 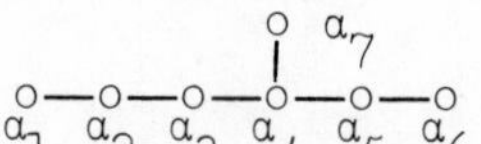 .

Maximal root: $\omega = \alpha_1 + 2\alpha_2 + 3\alpha_3 + 4\alpha_4 + 3\alpha_5 + 2\alpha_6 + 2\alpha_7$.

The possibilities for spaces of rank one are

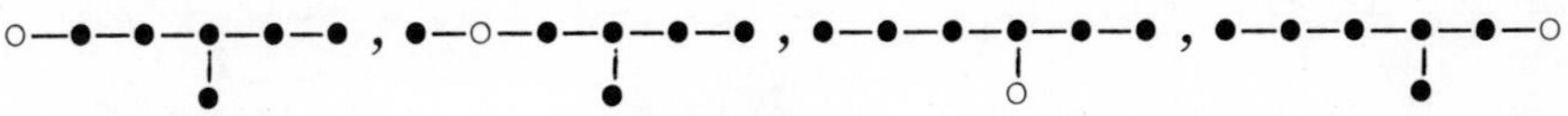

with dimensions 28 , 43 , 43 , 34 . Thus there are no spaces of rank one. The possible Σ_λ are the same as in case E_6 .

Assume α_6 black. Then the only diagram left with a possible dimension and admissible Σ_λ's is

(a) 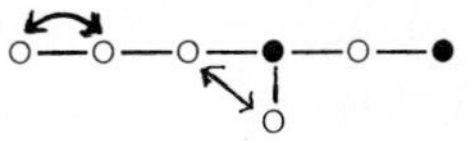 of dimension 64 .

Assume α_6 white, α_1 white, and α_2 black. Then one gets

(b) 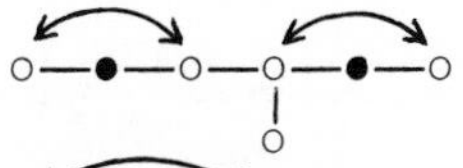 ,

(c) 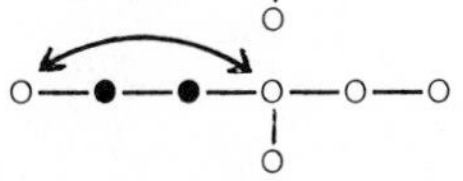 ,

both of dimension 64 .

Assume $\alpha_1 , \alpha_2 , \alpha_6$ white, and α_3 black. Then one gets

(d) 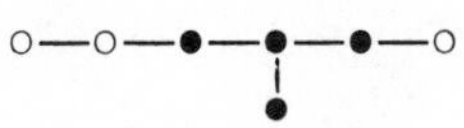 of dimension 54 .

Assume $\alpha_1 , \alpha_2 , \alpha_6$, and α_3 white. Then all roots have to be white, and we are in the case of maximal rank.

Assume α_6 white and α_1 black. Then we get

(e) 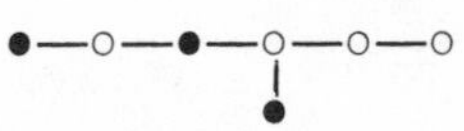 of dimension 64 .

Now we show that (a), (b), (c) are impossible. After

multiplying the bilinear form $(\ ,\ )$ with a suitable factor, we may assume that $(\alpha_i,\alpha_i)=2$ for $i=1,\dots,7$.

In case (a), we have $-\sigma(\alpha_1)=\alpha_2$, $-\sigma(\alpha_3)=\alpha_4+\alpha_7$, and it follows

$$-1=(\alpha_2,\alpha_3)=(-\sigma(\alpha_2),-\sigma(\alpha_3))=(\alpha_1,\alpha_4+\alpha_7)=0 .$$

In case (b): $-\sigma(\alpha_3)=\alpha_1+\alpha_2$, $-\sigma(\alpha_4)=\alpha_5+\alpha_6$,

$$-1=(\alpha_3,\alpha_4)=(\alpha_1+\alpha_2,\alpha_5+\alpha_6)=0 .$$

In case (c): $-\sigma(\alpha_5)=\alpha_5$, $-\sigma(\alpha_4)=\alpha_1+\alpha_2+\alpha_3$,

$$-1=(\alpha_4,\alpha_5)=(\alpha_1+\alpha_2+\alpha_3,\alpha_5)=0 .$$

Finally we obtain

$E_{7(-5)}$ ●—o—●—o—o—o (with ● attached below the fourth node), $-\sigma(\alpha_2)=\alpha_1+\alpha_2+\alpha_3$, $-\sigma(\alpha_4) = \alpha_3+\alpha_4+\alpha_7$, $-\sigma(\alpha_5)=\alpha_5$, $-\sigma(\alpha_6)=\alpha_6$. A computation shows that B_- has the Dynkin diagram o—o⇐o—o ($\bar\alpha_2$ $\bar\alpha_4$ $\bar\alpha_5$ $\bar\alpha_6$) and the root list of E_7 yields $m(\bar\alpha_2)=m(\bar\alpha_4)=4$, $m(\bar\alpha_5)=m(\bar\alpha_6)=1$.

$E_{7(-25)}$ o—o—●—●—●—o (with ● attached below the fourth node), $-\sigma(\alpha_1)=\alpha_1$, $-\sigma(\alpha_2)=\alpha_2+2\alpha_3+2\alpha_4+\alpha_5+\alpha_7$, $-\sigma(\alpha_6)=\alpha_3+2\alpha_4+2\alpha_5+\alpha_6+\alpha_7$, and one gets for B_-:

o—o⇐o ($\bar\alpha_6$ $\bar\alpha_2$ $\bar\alpha_1$), $m(\bar\alpha_6)=m(\bar\alpha_2)=8$, $m(\bar\alpha_1)=1$.

Satake diagrams of type E_8

Dynkin diagram: o—o—o—o—o—o—o (α_1 α_2 α_3 α_4 α_5 α_6 α_7, with o α_8 attached above α_5).

Maximal root: $2\alpha_1+3\alpha_2+4\alpha_3+5\alpha_4+6\alpha_5+4\alpha_6+2\alpha_7+3\alpha_8$.

The two possibilities 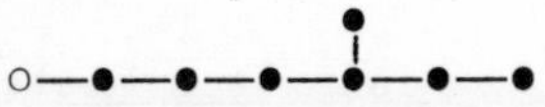 and

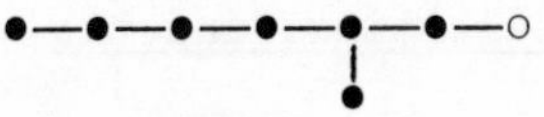 for spaces of rank one lead to dimensions

58 and 79 . Hence there are no spaces of rank one, and the Σ_λ are the same as in case E_6 . After checking dimensions, only the possibility

$E_{8(-24)}$ 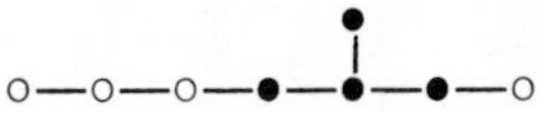

remains, and $-\sigma(\alpha_1) = \alpha_1$, $-\sigma(\alpha_2) = \alpha_2$, $-\sigma(\alpha_3) = \alpha_3 + 2\alpha_4 + 2\alpha_5 + \alpha_6 + \alpha_8$, $-\sigma(\alpha_7) = \alpha_4 + 2\alpha_5 + 2\alpha_6 + \alpha_7 + \alpha_8$. For B_- , one computes

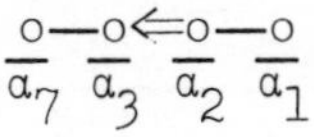

, $m(\bar{\alpha}_7) = m(\bar{\alpha}_3) = 8$,

$m(\bar{\alpha}_2) = m(\bar{\alpha}_1) = 1$.

5. Table of exceptional spaces

Here similar remarks as for Table 4 apply. The notation G , FI , FII , etc., is the one of É. Cartan. The space $F_{4(-20)}$ is the projective Cayley plane, sometimes denoted by $P_2(\mathbb{O})$.

From Table 4 and Table 8, we can draw the following remarkable consequence.

THEOREM 3.9. a) A compact simply connected symmetric space is uniquely determined by its root system and the multiplicities.

b) <u>A compact semisimple symmetric space is uniquely determined by its root system, the multiplicities, and the unit lattice</u>.

M		R	(Δ,m)	dim M
G	$G_{2(2)}$	G_2	1 1 o ⇚ o	8
F II	$F_{4(-20)}$	BC_1	◎ 8[7]	16
F I	$F_{4(4)}$	F_4	1 1 1 1 o—o⇐o—o	28
E IV	$E_{6(-26)}$	A_2	8 8 o—o	26
E III	$E_{6(-14)}$	BC_2	6 8[1] o⇒◎	32
E II	$E_{6(2)}$	F_4	2 2 1 1 o—o⇐o—o	40
E I	$E_{6(6)}$	E_6	o 1 | o—o—o—o—o 1 1 1 1 1	42
E VII	$E_{7(-25)}$	C_3	8 8 1 o—o⇐o	54
E VI	$E_{7(-5)}$	F_4	4 4 1 1 o—o⇐o—o	64
E V	$E_{7(7)}$	E_7	o 1 | o—o—o—o—o—o 1 1 1 1 1 1	70
E IX	$E_{8(-24)}$	F_4	8 8 1 1 o—o⇐o—o	112
E VIII	$E_{8(8)}$	E_8	o 1 | o—o—o—o—o—o—o 1 1 1 1 1 1 1	128

Table 8

M	Σ
A_q^R	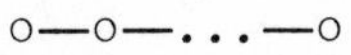
$A_n^{C,q} \quad (q < \frac{n+1}{2})$	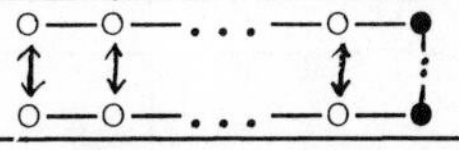
$A_{2q-1}^{C,q}$	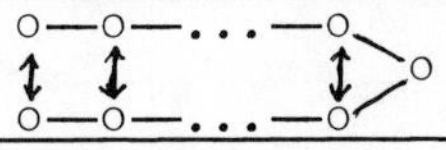
A_{2q+1}^{H}	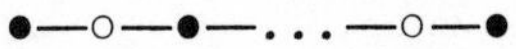
$B_n^{R,q}$	
C_q^R	
$C_n^{H,q} \quad (q < \frac{n}{2})$	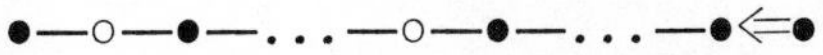
$C_{2q}^{H,q}$	
$D_n^{R,q} \quad (q < n-1)$	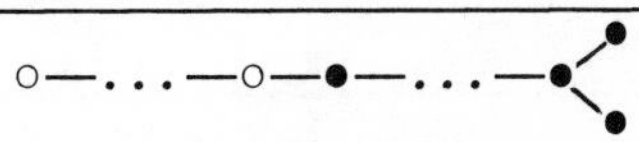
$D_{q+1}^{R,q}$	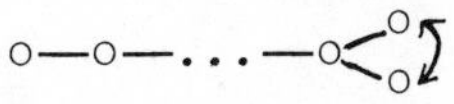
$D_q^{R,q}$	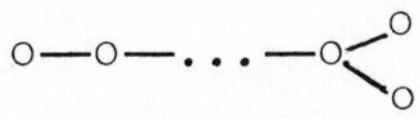
D_{2q}^{H}	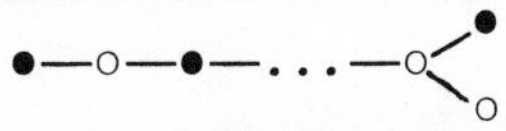
D_{2q+1}^{H}	
$G_{2(2)}$	
$F_{4(-20)}$	
$F_{4(4)}$	
$E_{6(-26)}$	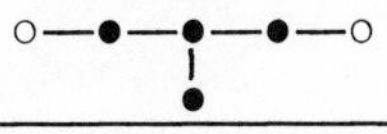

(continued)

$E_{6(-14)}$	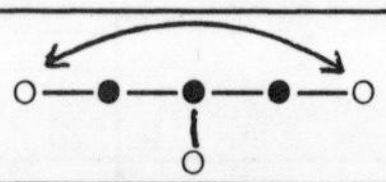
$E_{6(2)}$	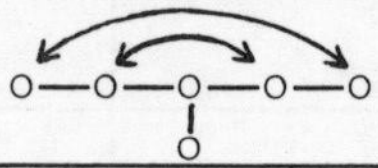
$E_{6(6)}$	
$E_{7(-25)}$	
$E_{7(-5)}$	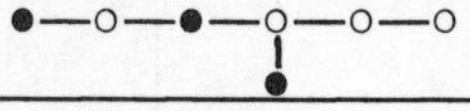
$E_{7(7)}$	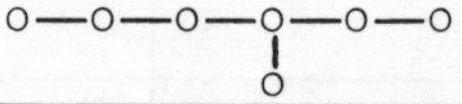
$E_{8(-24)}$	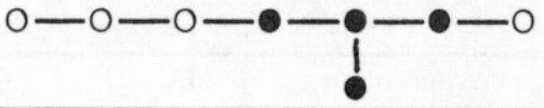
$E_{8(8)}$	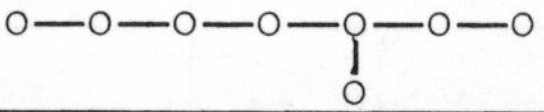

Table 9

If we understand by the root system of a space of non-compact type the root system of its compact dual, then a) is also true for those spaces. No a priori proof of Theorem 3.9 seems to be known.

For reference purposes, we also give the table of Satake diagrams. For the classical spaces, they follow in most cases from the structure of $\mathfrak{k}^{\mathfrak{A}}$ determined earlier. Proofs can be found in Araki [1].

§4 OUTER AUTOMORPHISMS

Let M be a compact simple (= irreducible) simply connected symmetric space, G its group of displacements, K the isotropy group of the base point. Also let N be the isotropy group of the base point in the full automorphism group $\mathrm{Aut}\, M$. We want to determine the finite group $E(M) = \mathrm{Aut}\, M/G$. Observe that relative to the metric given by the negative of the Ricci tensor, $\mathrm{Aut}\, M$ is the group of isometries of M and G is its identity component (IV, Proposition 1.4), thus $E(M) = I(M)/I_o(M)$.

PROPOSITION 4.1. a) $N \cong \mathrm{Aut}\, \mathfrak{M} \cong (\mathrm{Aut}\, \mathfrak{G})^\sigma$,

b) $E(M) \cong N/K \cong \mathrm{Aut}\, \mathfrak{M}/(\mathrm{Aut}\, \mathfrak{M})_o \cong (\mathrm{Aut}\, \mathfrak{G})^\sigma/((\mathrm{Aut}\, \mathfrak{G})^\sigma)_o$.

Proof. a) The first isomorphism follows from II, Theorem 4.12, and the second from the fact that $\mathfrak{G}$ is the standard imbedding of $\mathfrak{M}$.

b) We have $\mathrm{Aut}\, M = GN$, hence $E(M) = GN/G \cong N/G \cap N = N/K$. The two other automorphisms follow from a) and the fact that K is connected, since M is simply connected.

COROLLARY. *Let* M^* *be the noncompact dual of* M *and* G^* *its group of displacements. Then* $E(M^*) = \mathrm{Aut}\, M^*/G^* \cong E(M)$.

Observe that we didn't use the assumption that M is simple. This is, however, essential in

PROPOSITION 4.2. Let K^* be the linear representation of K in $\mathfrak{M}$, and $\mathbb{F}$ the set of all linear transformations of $\mathfrak{M}$ commuting with K^*. Then $K^* = (\mathrm{Aut}\ \mathfrak{M})_o$, and there are two possibilities:

a) The center of K is finite (i.e., K is semisimple) and $\mathbb{F} \cong \mathbb{R}$.

b) The center of K is one-dimensional and $\mathbb{F} \cong \mathbb{C}$.

In case b), the symmetry S_o around o belongs to K.

Proof. The Lie algebra $\mathfrak{K}^*$ of K^* consists of all inner derivations of $\mathfrak{M}$, since $\mathfrak{G}$ is isomorphic with the standard imbedding of $\mathfrak{M}$. Now $\mathfrak{M}$ has only inner derivations, and it follows $K^* = (\mathrm{Aut}\ \mathfrak{M})_o$. Since K^* acts irreducibly on $\mathfrak{M}$, it follows by Schur's Lemma that $\mathbb{F}$ is a field of finite dimension over $\mathbb{R}$, hence $\mathbb{F} \cong \mathbb{R}, \mathbb{C}$ or $\mathbb{H}$. Let $\mathfrak{C}^*$ be the center of $\mathfrak{K}^*$ and let $\mathbb{F}'$ be the subfield of $\mathbb{F}$ generated by $\mathbb{R}.\mathrm{id} \oplus \mathfrak{C}^*$. Then $\mathbb{F}'$ is abelian, hence $\dim_{\mathbb{R}} \mathbb{F}' \leq 2$ and $\dim \mathfrak{C}^* \leq 1$.

Let $J \in \mathbb{F}$ and $J^2 = -\mathrm{id}$. We will show that then $J \in \mathfrak{C}^*$, which completes the proof of a) and b). Let $\mathbb{F}_o$ be the set of elements of trace zero in $\mathbb{F}$. Then $\mathbb{F} = \mathbb{R}.\mathrm{id} \oplus \mathbb{F}_o$. Since

$\dim_{\mathbb{R}}\mathbb{F} \geq 2$, we have $\mathbb{F}\setminus\{0\} = e^{\mathbb{F}} \cong e^{\mathbb{R}} \times e^{\mathbb{F}_o}$, hence $e^{\mathbb{F}_o} \cong S^1$ or S^3 . Now $\mathbb{F}$ (and, therefore, also $\mathbb{F}_o$) is stable under taking transposes relative to (,) , because $\mathfrak{K}^*$ consists of skew-symmetric linear transformations. Assume that $0 \neq X \in \mathbb{F}_o$ is symmetric. Then $t \to e^{tX}$ is injective and $e^{\mathbb{R}X}$ is a geodesic in S^1 resp. S^3 , a contradiction. This shows that $\mathbb{F}_o$ consists of skew-symmetric linear transformations. Now the eigenvalues of J are $\pm\sqrt{-1}$ and since trace J is real, trace $J = 0$. Thus J is skew-symmetric, and we have for all $X,Y \in \mathfrak{M}$ and $U \in \mathfrak{K}$

$$([JX,Y],U) = -(JX,[U,Y]) = (X,J[U,Y]) = (X,[U,JY]) = -([X,JY],U) .$$

It follows $[JX,Y] + [X,JY] = 0$, and since $J[[X,Y],Z] = [[X,Y],JZ]$, we obtain

$$J[X,Y,Z] = J[[X,Y],Z] = [JX,Y,Z] + [X,JY,Z] + [X,Y,JZ] .$$

This shows that J is a derivation of $\mathfrak{M}$. Now $\mathfrak{M}$ has only inner derivations, and $\mathfrak{K}^*$ is the set of inner derivations of $\mathfrak{M}$, hence $J \in \mathfrak{K}^* \cap \mathbb{F} = \mathfrak{C}^*$.

Finally, in case b), we have $-\mathrm{id} = e^{\pi J} \in K^*$, which shows $S_o \in K$.

THEOREM 4.3. <u>Let</u> $K' = K \cup S_o K$. <u>Then</u> $N/K' \cong \mathrm{Aut}'K/\mathrm{Int}\ K$, <u>where</u> Aut'K <u>is the group of all automorphisms of</u> K <u>which extend to automorphisms of</u> G .

Proof. Since $K = N_o$, we can define a homomorphism $f\colon N \to \operatorname{Aut}'K$ by $f(n).k = nkn^{-1}$. Let $\varphi = \psi|K \in \operatorname{Aut}'K$ where $\psi \in \operatorname{Aut} G$. Then $\psi(\mathfrak{K}) = \mathfrak{K}$ implies $\psi(\mathfrak{M}) = \mathfrak{M}$. Hence $\psi|\mathfrak{M} \in \operatorname{Aut} \mathfrak{M}$ and for the corresponding element $n \in N$, we have $f(n) = \varphi$. Thus f is surjective. Assume now that $f(n) \in \operatorname{Int} K$, i.e., $nkn^{-1} = \ell k \ell^{-1}$ for all $k \in K$ and some $\ell \in K$. Then $\ell^{-1}n$ centralizes K; hence the linear transformation A of $\mathfrak{M}$ induced by $\ell^{-1}n$ belongs to $\mathbb{F}$ (see Proposition 4.2). Since A is an orthogonal transformation, we have $A = \pm \mathrm{id}$ in case a) and $A = e^{tJ} \in K^*$ in case b). In either case, it follows that $n \in K'$. Since clearly $f(K') = \operatorname{Int} K$, the assertion follows.

THEOREM 4.4. a) <u>Let $M = L^+$ be a compact simple simply connected Lie group considered as symmetric space. Then $E(M)$ is the direct product $E(L) \times \mathbb{Z}_2$ where $E(L) = \operatorname{Aut} L/\operatorname{Int} L$.</u>

b) <u>Let G be simple. Then $E(M)$ is the semidirect product $(\mathbb{Z}_2)^k \cdot F$ where</u>

$$2^k = \frac{|Z(M)|}{|Z(G)|} = \frac{|Z(M)|\,|Z(\tilde{G})^\sigma|}{|Z(\tilde{G})|} .$$

<u>The group F is isomorphic to the fixed point set E^σ of σ in $E = \operatorname{Aut} \tilde{G}/\operatorname{Int} \tilde{G}$ except for the real Grassmannian of oriented two-planes in $\mathbb{R}^8$, where $F = \mathbb{Z}_2$, and for the spaces D^H_{2q} $(q \geq 3)$, where $F = \{1\}$.</u>

<u>Proof</u>. a) By IV, Proposition 1.2, $\mathfrak{G} \cong \mathfrak{L} \times \mathfrak{L}$ and σ interchanges the factors. Now $\operatorname{Aut} \mathfrak{G}$ is the semidirect product of $\operatorname{Aut} \mathfrak{L} \times \operatorname{Aut} \mathfrak{L}$ and $\{id, \sigma\}$. Thus $\operatorname{Aut} \mathfrak{M} \cong (\operatorname{Aut} \mathfrak{G})^{\sigma} \cong (\operatorname{Aut} \mathfrak{L}) \times \{id, \sigma\}$, and the assertion follows.

b) Let $\overline{G} = (\operatorname{Aut} \mathfrak{G})_{o} \cong G/Z(G)$. Then $\overline{G}^{\sigma}$ is normal in $(\operatorname{Aut} \mathfrak{G})^{\sigma}$, and $\overline{G}^{\sigma}/(\overline{G}^{\sigma})_{o} \cong (\mathbf{Z}_2)^k$ (IV, Theorem 3.4) is normal in $E(M)$. To determine k, consider the commutative diagram

$$\begin{array}{ccc} G/K & \xrightarrow{\ \pi\ } & \overline{G}/\overline{G}^{\sigma} \\ & \varphi \searrow \quad \nearrow \psi & \\ & \overline{G}/(\overline{G}^{\sigma})_{o} & \end{array}$$

We have $M = G/K$ and $\overline{G}/\overline{G}^{\sigma} \cong M/Z(M)$ (see III, Proposition 2.4). Hence the fibre of π is $Z(M)$. Let $p\colon G \to G/Z(G) = \overline{G}$ be the canonical projection. Then $p^{-1}((\overline{G}^{\sigma})_{o}) = KZ(G)$ shows that the fibre of φ is $KZ(G)/K \cong Z(G)/K \cap Z(G) \cong Z(G)$, and the fibre of ψ is clearly $\overline{G}^{\sigma}/(\overline{G}^{\sigma})_{o}$. Since $G = \tilde{G}/Z(\tilde{G})^{\sigma}$ (IV, Corollary of Theorem 3.4), the formula for 2^k follows.

We show now by a case-by-case verification that $(\operatorname{Aut} \mathfrak{G})^{\sigma}$ has a subgroup F such that $(\operatorname{Aut} \mathfrak{G})^{\sigma}$ is the semidirect product $\overline{G}^{\sigma} \cdot F$.

<u>Case I</u>. $\operatorname{Aut} \mathfrak{G}$ is connected. Then the statement is trivially correct. Observe that $Z(G)$ is trivial since σ is an inner automorphism. Thus $E(M) = (\mathbf{Z}_2)^k$ where $2^k = |Z(M)|$. A glance at the classification shows that $k = 0,1$ and hence $E(M) \cong Z(M)$.

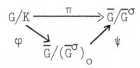

Case II. σ is outer. Then we set $F = \{id, \sigma\}$.

Case III. σ is inner, and $\mathfrak{G}$ has outer automorphisms.

a) $\mathfrak{G} = \mathfrak{SU}(n)$. Then $\sigma = \mathrm{Ad}\, I_{p,q}$ (see §2, 1°). Set $F = \{id, \tau\}$ where τ is complex conjugation.

b) $\mathfrak{G} = \mathfrak{SO}(2n)$, $n > 4$. Then $\sigma = \mathrm{Ad}\, I_{p,q}$ where q is even, or $\sigma = \mathrm{Ad}\, J_n$. In the first case, set $F = \{id, \mathrm{Ad}\, I_{2n-1,1}\}$. If $\sigma = \mathrm{Ad}\, J_n$ and n is odd, set $F = \{id, \mathrm{Ad}\, I_{n,n}\}$. Finally, if $n = 2q$ is even, we have $M = D^H_{2q}$, $G = SO(4q)/\{\pm e\}$ and $K = U(2q)/\{\pm e\}$. Therefore $\mathrm{Aut}\, K/\mathrm{Int}\, K = \mathbb{Z}_2$, and by Theorem 4.3, $|E(M)| \leq 2$ since $S_o \in K$. On the other hand, $Z(M) = \mathbb{Z}_2$ and $Z(G)$ is trivial; hence it follows that $2^k = 2$ and $E(M) = \mathbb{Z}_2$. Therefore we have to set $F = \{id\}$.

c) $\mathfrak{G} = \mathfrak{SO}(8)$. Then $\sigma = \mathrm{Ad}\, I_{6,2}$ or $\sigma = \mathrm{Ad}\, I_{4,4}$, corresponding to the Grassmannians of oriented two-planes resp. four-planes in $\mathbb{R}^8$. We have $G = SO(8)/\{\pm e\}$, and $K = SO(6) \times SO(2)/\{\pm e\}$ in the first case. Now $\mathrm{Aut}\, K/\mathrm{Int}\, K = \mathbb{Z}_2 \times \mathbb{Z}_2$, therefore $|E(M)| \leq 4$ by Theorem 4.3. The center of M is $\mathbb{Z}_2$ and the center of G is trivial, hence $2^k = 2$. Also, the outer automorphism $\tau = \mathrm{Ad}\, I_{7,1}$ belongs to $(\mathrm{Aut}\, \mathfrak{G})^\sigma$ so that $E(M) = \mathbb{Z}_2 \times \mathbb{Z}_2$, and we set $F = \{id, \tau\}$.

In the second case, we realize $\mathbb{R}^8$ as the underlying vector space of $\mathbb{O} = \mathbb{H} \oplus \mathbb{H}\ell$ (see §2, (1)). Then $-I_{4,4}$ is the reflection S in $\mathbb{H}$ given by $S(x + y\ell) = x - y\ell$; hence

$\sigma = \mathrm{Ad}\,S$. Let F be the subgroup of $\mathrm{Aut}\,\mathfrak{S}\mathfrak{O}(8)$ generated by π and θ as in Theorem 2.2. Clearly π and σ commute. To show that σ and θ commute, it suffices to do this for the transformations $X_{a,b}: x \to (x,b)a - (x,a)b$. We have $\sigma(X_{a,b}) = X_{Sa,Sb}$, and the assertion follows by a straightforward computation similar to the one in the proof of 5° in §2, using the formulas (2), (3), (4), and (7) of §2.

Since $Z(M) = \mathbb{Z}_2 \times \mathbb{Z}_2$ and $Z(G)$ is trivial, $E(M)$ is the semidirect product of $\mathbb{Z}_2 \times \mathbb{Z}_2$ and $F \cong \mathfrak{S}_3$, and one can show that $E(M) \cong \mathfrak{S}_4$.

d) $\mathfrak{G} = \mathfrak{E}_6$. By the results of §3, in particular (4) of §3, σ is conjugate to $\mathrm{Ad}\exp X_6$ or $\mathrm{Ad}\exp \frac{1}{2}(X_1 + X_5)$. Here $X_0 = 0, X_1, \ldots, X_6$ are the vertices of the cell $\alpha_i > 0$, $(i = 1,\ldots,6)$, $-\alpha_0 < 1$. Set $F = \{id, \tau\}$ where τ is the normal extension (see §3, $\underline{\underline{2}}$, p. 129 f) of

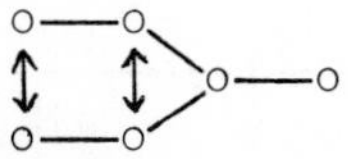

We collect our results in the following table. The spaces where $E(M)$ is trivial are not listed. $\mathbb{D}_4$ is the dihedral group of order 8 and $\mathfrak{S}_n$ the group of permutations of n letters.

M	2^k	F	E(M)
$A_1^R = A_1^{C,1} = S^2$	2	1	$\mathbb{Z}_2$
A_q^R $(q \geq 2$ even$)$	1	$\mathbb{Z}_2$	$\mathbb{Z}_2$
A_q^R $(q \geq 3$ odd$)$	2	$\mathbb{Z}_2$	$\mathbb{Z}_2 \times \mathbb{Z}_2$
$A_n^{C,q}$ $(1 \leq q < \frac{n+1}{2})$	1	$\mathbb{Z}_2$	$\mathbb{Z}_2$
$A_{2q-1}^{C,q}$ $(q \geq 2)$	2	$\mathbb{Z}_2$	$\mathbb{Z}_2 \times \mathbb{Z}_2$
A_{2q+1}^H $(q \geq 1)$	1	$\mathbb{Z}_2$	$\mathbb{Z}_2$
$B_n^{R,q}$ $(1 \leq q \leq n)$	2	1	$\mathbb{Z}_2$
C_q^R $(q \geq 1)$	2	1	$\mathbb{Z}_2$
$C_{2q}^{H,q}$ $(q \geq 1)$	2	1	$\mathbb{Z}_2$
$D_n^{R,q}$ $(q$ odd, $q < n \geq 2)$	1	$\mathbb{Z}_2$	$\mathbb{Z}_2$
$D_n^{R,q}$ $(q$ even, $q < n \geq 3)$	2	$\mathbb{Z}_2$	$\mathbb{Z}_2 \times \mathbb{Z}_2$
$D_q^{R,q}$ $(q \geq 3$ odd$)$	2	$\mathbb{Z}_2$	$\mathbb{Z}_2 \times \mathbb{Z}_2$
$D_q^{R,q}$ $(4 \neq q \geq 2$ even$)$	4	$\mathbb{Z}_2$	$\mathbb{D}_4$
$D_4^{R,4}$	4	$\mathfrak{S}_3$	$\mathfrak{S}_4$
D_{2q}^H $(q \geq 3)$	2	1	$\mathbb{Z}_2$
D_{2q+1}^H $(q \geq 1)$	1	$\mathbb{Z}_2$	$\mathbb{Z}_2$
$E_{6(i)}$ $(i = -26, -14, 2, 6)$	1	$\mathbb{Z}_2$	$\mathbb{Z}_2$
$E_7(i)$ $(i = -25, 7)$	2	1	$\mathbb{Z}_2$

Table 10

NOTES

§1 The classification of semisimple Lie algebras resp. reduced root systems, due to Killing and É. Cartan, is by now standard; a modern exposition can be found in Jacobson [1]. The classification of non-reduced root systems is mentioned in Serre [1].

§2 For the standard facts on classical groups, we refer to Chevalley [1]. The classification of involutive automorphisms is similar to the one in Lister [1] for the complex case. The treatment of the triality automorphism is taken from Walde [1]. The classification, including the determination of the root systems, goes back to É. Cartan [2] (the multiplicities given there for the Grassmann manifolds and the spaces D^H_{2q+1} seem to be incorrect).

§3 Theorem 3.1 is a special case of a theorem by Borel and de Siebenthal [1] on maximal subgroups of maximal rank of compact Lie groups. Theorem 3.2 is a special case of a result of de Siebenthal [1] on conjugacy in compact non-connected Lie groups. The approach to the classification of the exceptional spaces is similar to Wolf's [1]; it works of course also for the classical spaces. However, we have preferred to give a more elementary and independent classification in the classical case. For a more systematic treatment of outer automorphisms, see de Siebenthal [1]; the one here seems shorter, especially since the classical spaces are already known. Satake diagrams have been introduced by Satake [1]. The material in 3 is taken from there and Araki [1]. In this paper, Araki gave a classification of symmetric spaces based on the notion of a root system with involution. Our discussion in 4 follows his; however, since the symmetric spaces are already known and only the root systems have to be determined, considerable shortcuts are possible. All the results are already contained in É. Cartan [2].

§4 Proposition 4.2 and Theorem 4.3 which goes back to É. Cartan are taken from Wolf [1]. The order of E(M) is determined in É. Cartan [2] for all compact simple spaces.

CHAPTER VIII

HERMITIAN SPACES AND JORDAN ALGEBRAS

In this chapter, no complete proofs are given.

§1 HERMITIAN SYMMETRIC SPACES

1. Complex manifolds

A complex structure on a manifold M consists of an atlas $(U_\alpha, \varphi_\alpha)$ of local coordinate systems, such that φ_α is a diffeomorphism of U_α onto some open subset of $\mathbb{C}^n$ and the transition functions between any two coordinate systems are holomorphic. Let $(z_1, \ldots, z_n) = \varphi_\alpha$, and define an endomorphism J of $T(M)$ by $J(\frac{\partial}{\partial x_i}) = \frac{\partial}{\partial y_i}$; $J(\frac{\partial}{\partial y_i}) = -\frac{\partial}{\partial x_i}$, where $z_i = x_i + \sqrt{-1}\, y_i$. Clearly $J^2 = -\mathrm{id}$. J is called the associated almost complex structure. It satisfies the integrability condition $S(X,Y) = [X,Y] + J[JX,Y] + J[X,JY] - [JX,JY] = 0$. A theorem of Newlander and Nirenberg states that a manifold with an almost complex structure J satisfying $S = 0$ has a complex structure with J as the associated almost complex structure. A manifold with a complex structure is called a complex manifold.

A Hermitian metric on a complex manifold is a Riemannian metric g such that $g(JX,JY) = g(X,Y)$. Then $\Omega(X,Y) = g(X,JY)$ is an exterior two-form, and g is called Kählerian if $d\Omega = 0$.

2. Hermitian symmetric spaces

Let M be a connected symmetric space with a complex structure (all symmetric spaces in this chapter are connected). M is called semicomplex if the symmetry around every point is holomorphic. M is called complex if the multiplication map $(x,y) \to x \cdot y$ is holomorphic. M is called Hermitian if it is semicomplex and there exists a Hermitian metric invariant under all symmetries. M is called anticomplex if $R(JX,Y) + R(X,JY) = 0$, where R is the curvature tensor.

PROPOSITION 1.1. a) *A semicomplex symmetric space is complex if and only if* $R(JX,Y) = R(X,JY)$.

b) *A Hermitian symmetric space is Kählerian and anticomplex.*

Thus a Hermitian space can be complex only if it is flat. The product $x \cdot y$ is holomorphic in y, but not in x (although it is real analytic).

Now let M be Hermitian and semisimple, G its group of displacements, J_o the restriction of J to $\mathfrak{m} = T_o(M)$, and $\mathfrak{K}^*$ the linear representation of $\mathfrak{K}$ on $\mathfrak{M}$. Then J_o centralizes $\mathfrak{K}^*$, and by Proposition 1.1 b), it follows that J_o is a derivation of $\mathfrak{M}$; hence $J_o \in \mathfrak{K}^*$ (see also VII, Proposition 5.2). Thus the center of K is not discrete, and $S_o \in K$. If M is compact, then K as the centralizer of the circle group $\exp \mathbb{R}J_o$ is connected. Since σ is inner, the center of G is trivial. Hence $M = G/K$ is simply connected and we have

THEOREM 1.2. Let $M = G/K$ be a semisimple Hermitian symmetric space. Then S_o belongs to the center of K and K is not semisimple. M is simply connected.

From VII, Proposition 5.2, one gets

THEOREM 1.3. Let $M = G/K$ be a simple simply connected symmetric space of compact or noncompact type. Then M is Hermitian if and only if K is not semisimple.

From our classification, we obtain the following list of simple compact Hermitian spaces.

	M	(Δ, m)
I	$M(q, p+q; \mathbb{C})$	2 2 2 2(p-q) o—o—...—o⇒◎ [1] $(q < p)$
		2 2 2 1 o—o—...—o⇐o $(q = p)$
II	D_n^H	4 4 4 1 o—o—...—o⇐o $(n = 2q)$
		4 4 4 4 o—o—...—o⇒◎ [1] $(n = 2q+1)$
III	C_q^R	1 1 1 1 o—o—...—o⇐o
IV	$\tilde{M}(2, d+4; \mathbb{R})$	d 1 o⇐o
	$E_{6(-14)}$	6 8 o⇒◎ [1]
	$E_{7(-25)}$	8 8 1 o—o⇐o

Table 1

The numbers I-IV correspond to Siegel's notation. We remark that the isomorphisms noted earlier (VII, §2, 5) are also isomorphisms of Hermitian symmetric spaces.

3. The Bergman metric

We give a review of the theory of the Bergman kernel.

Let D be a bounded domain in $\mathbb{C}^n$, $L^2(D)$ the Hilbert space of square integrable functions on D with the scalar product

$$(f,g) = \int_D \bar{f}(z)g(z)dz\,,$$

and $\mathfrak{H}(D)$ the subspace of holomorphic functions. Then $\mathfrak{H}(D)$ is closed in $L^2(D)$ and therefore itself a Hilbert space. Let $\varphi_0, \varphi_1, \varphi_2, \ldots$ be a complete orthonormal system for $\mathfrak{H}(D)$. Then

$$K(z,w) = \sum_{n=0}^{\infty} \varphi_n(z)\overline{\varphi_n(\bar{w})}$$

converges uniformly on each compact subset of $D \times D$ and is independent of the choice of the orthonormal system. Furthermore

$$f(z) = \int_D K(z,\bar{w})f(w)dw$$

for every $f \in \mathfrak{H}(D)$. The function K is called the <u>Bergman kernel function</u> of D. We put $B(z) = K(z,\bar{z})$ and

$$g = \mathrm{Re}\Big(\sum_{i,j} \frac{\partial^2 \log B}{\partial z_i \partial \bar{z}_j}\, dz_i d\bar{z}_j\Big)\,.$$

Then g is a hermitian metric on D which is Kählerian.

Let φ be a biholomorphic transformation of D, and $j(\varphi) = \det\Big(\frac{\partial \varphi_i}{\partial z_j}\Big)$ the complex Jacobian. One deduces from the transformation formula $B = (B \circ \varphi)|j(\varphi)|^2$ that φ is an isometry relative to the Bergman metric. Hence the group

$H(D)$ of biholomorphic transformations of D is a closed subgroup of the group of isometries $I(D)$. We say that D is homogeneous if $H(D)$ is transitive on D. In that case $\rho = 2g$, where ρ is the Ricci tensor of g.

4. Bounded symmetric domains

A bounded domain D is said to be symmetric if for every point z in D there exists a biholomorphic involutive transformation of D having z as isolated fixed point. The fundamental theorem about such domains is

THEOREM 1.4. a) With the Bergman metric, a bounded symmetric domain is a Hermitian symmetric space of noncompact type.

b) Every Hermitian symmetric space of noncompact type is isomorphic to a bounded symmetric domain.

Part a) is an easy consequence of the properties of the Bergman metric. Part b) has been proven by É. Cartan using the classification, and by Harish-Chandra. We sketch the idea of his proof. Let P be a Hermitian symmetric space of noncompact type and $\mathfrak{G}^* = \mathfrak{K} \oplus \mathfrak{P}$ the Lie algebra of its group of displacements G^*. Let $\mathfrak{P}_C = \mathfrak{P}_+ \oplus \mathfrak{P}_-$ be the decomposition into the $\pm\sqrt{-1}$-eigenspaces of the complex structure J_o on $\mathfrak{P}$. Then $\mathfrak{P}_\pm$ are abelian subspaces which are stable under $\mathfrak{K}$. Let G_C be the centerfree group with Lie algebra $(\mathfrak{G}^*)_C$ and $K_C, G^*, P_\pm$ the subgroups corresponding to $\mathfrak{K}_C, \mathfrak{G}^*, \mathfrak{P}_\pm$. Then $\exp: \mathfrak{P}_\pm \to P_\pm$ is a diffeomorphism, and the product map $P_- \times K_C \times P_+ \to G_C$ is a diffeomorphism onto an open submanifold of G_C containing G^*. Moreover, $G^*K_CP_+$ is open in $P_-K_CP_+$ and $G^* \cap K_CP_+ = K$. Let $\zeta: G^* \to P_-$ be defined by $g \in \zeta(g)K_CP_+$. Then $P \cong \exp(\mathfrak{P}) \subset G^*$ and $g \to \log \zeta(g) \in \mathfrak{P}_-$ gives the desired realization of P as a bounded symmetric domain. A detailed proof can be found in Helgason [1].

We finally mention the Borel imbedding. Let $\mathfrak{M} = \sqrt{-1}\,\mathfrak{P}$ be the dual of $\mathfrak{P}$, and $\mathfrak{G} = \mathfrak{K} \oplus \mathfrak{M}$. Let G be the corresponding subgroup of G_C. Then $M = G/K$ is the compact dual of P. The map $f: M \to G_C/K_CP_+$ given by $f(gk) = gK_CP_+$ is a G-equivariant diffeomorphism. Now $P \cong \zeta(P) \subset P_- \subset G_C/K_CP_+$ gives the Borel imbedding of P into M as an open submanifold. The complex structure of P is the one induced from M.

§2 JORDAN ALGEBRAS

1. Domains of positivity

Let (x,y) denote the inner product in a Euclidean vector space X. An open subset Y of X is called a domain of positivity if

(i) $(x,y) > 0$ for all $x,y \in Y$;

(ii) $(x,y) > 0$ for some $x \in X$ and all $0 \neq y \in \overline{Y}$ implies $x \in Y$.

Note that Y is a convex cone in X , and $x \in Y$ if and only if $(y,x) \neq 0$ for all $y \in \overline{Y}$ with $y \neq 0$.

We denote by Aut Y the group of all linear transformations of X leaving Y invariant. Y is called homogeneous if Aut Y is transitive on Y .

A norm on Y is a positive C^∞-function N on Y such that

$$N(Ay) = |\det A| N(y) \tag{1}$$

for all $A \in \text{Aut } Y$ and $y \in Y$. If we put

$$B(y) = \int_Y e^{-(x,y)} dx \ ,$$

then the transformation formula for integrals shows that $N(y) = \frac{c}{B(y)}$ is a norm on Y . Thus every domain of positivity has a norm, and it is clear from the definition that N is unique up to a constant factor if Y is homogeneous. The "Bergman metric"

$$g = \Sigma \frac{\partial^2 \log B}{\partial x_i \partial x_k} dx_i dx_k$$

is a Riemannian metric on Y which is invariant under Aut Y .

For any $y \in Y$ let $y^\# = -\text{grad} \log B(y)$. Then one has

$$(Ay)^{\#} = ({}^{t}A)^{-1}y^{\#} \tag{2}$$

for $A \in \operatorname{Aut} Y$. Note also that $\operatorname{Aut} Y$ is stable under taking transposes. Since all homotheties $y \to \lambda y$ where $\lambda > 0$ belong to $\operatorname{Aut} Y$, we have $(\lambda y)^{\#} = \lambda^{-1} y^{\#}$ and also $B(\lambda y) = \lambda^{-n} B(y)$. Let Y_α be the hypersurface $\{y \in Y: N(y) = \alpha\}$. Then Y_α is convex, since the matrix of second derivatives of $\log B$ is positive definite. Hence Y_α lies on one side of its tangent plane, and the origin on the other. There exists $y \in Y_\alpha$ realizing the minimum of the distances between 0 and Y_α. Then y is normal to Y_α at y, i.e., we have $y = \lambda y^{\#}$ with $\lambda > 0$. Putting $e = \frac{y}{\sqrt{\lambda}}$, we get $e^{\#} = e$. We choose the constant c in $N = \frac{c}{B}$ such that $N(e) = 1$.

Suppose now that Y is homogeneous. Then it follows from (1) and (2) that $y \to y^{\#}$ is an involutive isometry of Y having e as isolated fixed point and hence Y is a Riemannian symmetric space. Since Y as a convex cone is contractible, we get from IV, Corollary 1 of Theorem 1.6:

THEOREM 2.1. _A homogeneous domain of positivity is a Riemannian symmetric space, isomorphic to the product of a Euclidean space and a space of noncompact type._

2. Formal real Jordan Algebras

Let $\mathfrak{A}$ be a Jordan algebra over $\mathbb{R}$. Recall the notations $L(x)$ for the left multiplication with x in $\mathfrak{A}$ and $P(x) = 2L(x)^2 - L(x^2)$. The exponential function in $\mathfrak{A}$ is $e^x = \sum_0^\infty \frac{x^n}{n!}$. The set of invertible elements in $\mathfrak{A}$ is a symmetric space with $x \cdot y = P(x)y^{-1}$ (see II, §1). A Jordan algebra is called <u>formal real</u> if the bilinear form $(x,y) = \operatorname{trace} L(xy)$ is positive definite.

Let Y be a homogeneous domain of positivity as above. Then

$$(u,v,w) = \frac{1}{2}\Sigma \frac{\partial^3 \log N(e)}{\partial y_i \partial y_j \partial y_l} u_i v_j w_k$$

is a symmetric trilinear form on X, and we define a multiplication uv by

$$(uv,w) = (u,v,w) \tag{3}$$

for all $w \in X$. Let $\mathfrak{A}(Y)$ be the algebra with underlying vector space X and the multiplication defined by (3).

THEOREM 2.2. *For a homogeneous domain of positivity, $\mathfrak{A}(Y)$ is a formal real Jordan algebra with unit element e, and Y is (as a symmetric space) equal to the connected component of e of invertible elements of $\mathfrak{A}$. Conversely, for a formal real Jordan algebra $\mathfrak{A}$, the connected component $Y(\mathfrak{A})$ of e of*

<u>invertible elements in</u> $\mathfrak{a}$ <u>is a homogeneous domain of positivity relative to the bilinear form</u> trace $L(xy)$. <u>We have</u> $\mathfrak{a}(Y(\mathfrak{a})) = \mathfrak{a}$ <u>and</u> $Y(\mathfrak{a}(Y)) = Y$.

The proof can be found in Koecher [2]. In terms of $\mathfrak{a}$, we have $y^{\#} = y^{-1}$, $N(y) = (\det P(y))^{1/2}$ and $(x,y) =$ trace $L(xy)$. Also $Y = e^{\mathfrak{a}}$ since the exponential map of Y as a symmetric space at the point e is just the exponential function in $\mathfrak{a}$, and one can show that $Y = \{y \in \mathfrak{a}: L(y)$ positive definite$\}$. Finally $\overline{Y} = \mathfrak{a}^2 = \{x^2: x \in \mathfrak{a}\}$.

Let $\mathfrak{a}$ be a formal real Jordan algebra. The bilinear form $(x,y) = \operatorname{trace} L(xy)$ satisfies $(xy,z) = (x,yz)$; hence a well-known argument shows that $\mathfrak{a}$ decomposes uniquely up to order into a sum $\mathfrak{a}_1 \oplus \ldots \oplus \mathfrak{a}_k$ of simple ideals. This yields a corresponding decomposition for the domain of positivity $Y(\mathfrak{a})$. Thus we assume from now on that $\mathfrak{a}$ is simple. An idempotent $c \in \mathfrak{a}$ is called primitive if it cannot be decomposed into $c = c_1 + c_2$ where c_i are idempotents and $c_1 c_2 = 0$. The set $\{c_1, \ldots, c_r\}$ of idempotents is called a complete orthogonal system of primitive idempotents if each c_i is a primitive idempotent, $c_i c_j = 0$ for $i \neq j$, and $\Sigma\, c_i = e$. It follows from the Jordan identity that for any idempotent c the eigenvalues of $L(c)$ are $0, \frac{1}{2}, 1$. For a complete orthogonal system $\{c_1, \ldots, c_r\}$, we put

$\mathcal{A}_{ij} = \{x \in \mathcal{A}\colon\ c_i x = c_j x = \frac{1}{2} x\}$. Then

$$\mathcal{A} = \sum_{i=1}^{r} \mathbb{R}.c_i \oplus \sum_{i<j} \mathcal{A}_{ij}$$

is an orthogonal direct sum decomposition. The number r is called the <u>degree</u> of $\mathcal{A}$. The spaces $\mathcal{A}_{ij}$ have the same dimension d . We say that $\mathcal{A}$ is of type (r,d) .

Let $\mathfrak{M}$ be the Lts of $Y(\mathcal{A})$ at e . By II, §2, (6), $\mathfrak{M} = \mathcal{A}$ as a vector space and the Lie triple product is given by $[x,y,z] = x(yz) - y(xz)$. Also $\mathfrak{M} = \mathbb{R}.e \oplus \mathfrak{M}'$ where $\mathfrak{M}' = \{x \in \mathcal{A}\colon \text{trace } L(x) = 0\}$ is a decomposition into ideals. Let $\mathfrak{A} = \{\Sigma\, a_i c_i\colon\ a_i \in \mathbb{R} \text{ and } \Sigma\, a_i = 0\}$. Then $\mathfrak{A} \subset \mathfrak{M}'$, and for $H = \Sigma\, a_i c_i \in \mathfrak{A}$ and $X_{ij} \in \mathcal{A}_{ij}$ a simple computation shows

$$[X_{ij}, H, H] = \left(\frac{a_i - a_j}{2}\right)^2 X_{ij} \ .$$

Hence we get

PROPOSITION 2.3. <u>The space</u> $\mathfrak{M}'$ <u>of elements of trace</u> 0 <u>in a simple formal real Jordan algebra</u> $\mathcal{A}$ <u>of type</u> (r,d) <u>is a simple Lie triple system of noncompact type of rank</u> $r-1$ <u>and with root system</u>

$$A_{r-1}\colon\ \overset{d}{\circ}\!-\!\!\!-\overset{d}{\circ}\!-\!\!\!-\cdots-\!\!\!-\overset{d}{\circ}\ .$$

Excluding the case $r = 1$ where $\mathcal{A} = \mathbb{R}$, we have by the results of Chapter VII the following possibilities: $r = 2$,

$d \geq 1$; $r \geq 3$, $d = 1,2,4$; $r = 3$, $d = 8$. It is easy to verify that these really occur by constructing the corresponding Jordan algebras:

a) $r = 2$, $d \geq 1$. Let $\mathfrak{a} = \mathbb{R}.e \oplus \mathbb{R}^{d+1}$, and define the product on $\mathfrak{a}$ such that e is the unit element and $uv = (u,v)e$ for $u,v \in \mathbb{R}^{d+1}$.

b) $r \geq 3$, $d = 1,2,4,8$: Let $\mathfrak{a}$ be the Jordan algebra $\mathcal{H}(r, \mathbb{K})$ of Hermitian $r \times r$-matrices over $\mathbb{K} = \mathbb{R}, \mathbb{C}, \mathbb{H}$ or $\mathbb{O}$ ($r = 3$ in the last case) with the product $a \circ b = \frac{1}{2}(ab + ba)$.

By the classification of simple formal real Jordan algebras (Braun-Koecher [1]), every such Jordan algebra is isomorphic to one of the algebras listed above. Clearly (r,d) determine $\mathfrak{a}$ uniquely.

Let $Y = Y(\mathfrak{a})$ and $Y_1 = \{y \in Y: N(y) = 1\}$. Then Y_1 is a symmetric subspace of Y and its Lts is $\mathfrak{M}'$. Also $Y \cong \mathbb{R} \times Y_1$. From the classification above we get:

THEOREM 2.4. <u>Let</u> M <u>be a simple symmetric space of noncompact type. Then</u> $\mathbb{R} \times M$ <u>is isomorphic to a domain of positivity if and only if the root system of</u> M <u>is of type</u> A .

3. Half spaces

Let Y be the domain of positivity of a formal real Jordan algebra $\mathfrak{a}$ and let H be the subset $\mathfrak{a} \oplus \sqrt{-1}\, Y =$

$\{x+\sqrt{-1}\,y : x \in \mathfrak{a}, y \in Y\}$ of the complexification $\mathfrak{a}_C$ of $\mathfrak{a}$. We call H the <u>halfspace</u> belonging to $\mathfrak{a}$. If $\mathfrak{a} = \mathbb{R}$ and Y is the set of positive real numbers, then H is the upper half plane in $\mathbb{C}$.

Clearly H is an open subset of $\mathfrak{a}_C$. If $z = x+\sqrt{-1}\,y \in H$, then $L(y)$ is symmetric and positive definite; hence $L(y) = B^2$ where B is symmetric and positive definite. Then $B^{-1}L(x)B$ is symmetric and has therefore real eigenvalues. It follows $0 \neq \det(B^{-1}L(x)B^{-1} + \sqrt{-1}\,\mathrm{id}) = \det B^{-2} \det L(z)$, therefore z is invertible. From the formula $P(z^{-1})P(z+w)P(w^{-1}) = P(z^{-1}+w^{-1})$, one gets $P(z^{-1})P(y)\overline{P(z^{-1})} = P(\mathrm{Im}\, z^{-1})$. Hence $\pm z^{-1} \in H$. But since $-(\sqrt{-1}\,e)^{-1} = \sqrt{-1}\,e \in H$, it follows that $z \to -z^{-1}$ is a holomorphic involution of H. The only fixed point is $\sqrt{-1}\,e$, since $z^2 = x^2 - y^2 + 2\sqrt{-1}\,xy = e$ implies $x = 0$ and $y = e$. Note also that the group of biholomorphic transformations of H generated by $z \to Az+u$ where $A \in \mathrm{Aut}\, Y$ and $u \in X$ is transitive on H.

Now let $\varphi(z) = (z-\sqrt{-1}e)(z+\sqrt{-1}e)^{-1}$ for $z \in H$. One checks that $\psi(z) = -\sqrt{-1}(z+e)(z-e)^{-1}$ is the inverse of φ, thus φ is a biholomorphic map of H onto a domain $D = \varphi(H)$. For $z \in D$ we have $-\sqrt{-1}e - 2\sqrt{-1}(z-e)^{-1} \in H$; hence $A = \mathrm{id} + L((z-e)^{-1}) + L((\bar{z}-e)^{-1})$ is negative definite. It follows

$$0 > (\bar{z}-e, A.(z-e)) = (\bar{z},z) - (e,e) ,$$

i.e., $\|z\|^2 < (e,e)$, and D is bounded. This leads to the following

THEOREM 2.5. *The halfspace* H *belonging to a formal real Jordan algebra is a Hermitian symmetric space of noncompact type which is isomorphic to the bounded symmetric domain* $D = \varphi(H)$ *under the map* $\varphi\colon z \to (z - \sqrt{-1}e)(z + \sqrt{-1}e)^{-1}$.

PROPOSITION 2.6. *Let* $\mathfrak{A}$ *be a simple formal real Jordan algebra of type* (r,d) . *Then the corresponding half space has rank* r *and root system*

$$C_r\colon \overset{d}{\circ}\!-\!\overset{d}{\circ}\!-\cdots-\!\overset{d}{\circ}\Leftarrow\overset{1}{\circ}$$

From the classification we get

THEOREM 2.7. *Let* M *be a simple symmetric space of noncompact type. Then* M *is isomorphic to a halfspace if and only if its root system is of type* C *and the long roots have multiplicity one*.

Now let $D = \varphi(H)$ be as above and let $U = \{z \in \mathfrak{A}_C :$ $[L(z), L(\bar{z})] = 0$ and $z\bar{z} = e\}$. Then U is a subset of the boundary of D . It turns out that $U = \overline{\varphi(\mathfrak{A})} = \exp(\sqrt{-1}\,\mathfrak{A})$ is the compact dual of Y. Also U is the Bergman-Šilov boundary of D. This leads to the following characterization of halfspaces among Hermitian symmetric spaces.

THEOREM 2.8. *Let M be a simple Hermitian symmetric space of noncompact type. Then the following conditions are equivalent:*

a) *M is isomorphic to a half space;*

b) *the dimension of M is twice the dimension of its Bergman-Šilov boundary;*

c) *the root system of M is reduced.*

4. Primitive idempotents

Let $\mathfrak{a}$ be a real Jordan algebra and $V = \{v \in \mathfrak{a}: v^2 = e\}$ the set of involutive elements in $\mathfrak{a}$. Clearly $v \in V$ iff $v^{-1} = v$, and from $(x \cdot y)^{-1} = (P(x)y^{-1})^{-1} = P(x)^{-1}y = x^{-1} \cdot y^{-1}$ it follows that V is a closed subspace of the symmetric space of invertible elements of $\mathfrak{a}$. Hence V is itself a symmetric space generally not connected. Let I be the set of idempotents in $\mathfrak{a}$. Then $c \to e - 2c$ defines a bijection of I onto V; the inverse is $v \to \frac{e-v}{2}$. Transferring the symmetric space structure from V to I, one gets $c \cdot d = d - 8cd + 8c(cd) = P(e-2c)d$, for $c, d \in I$. Also note that $P(e-2c)$ is an involutive automorphism of $\mathfrak{a}$.

For any $c \in I$, we have the decomposition $\mathfrak{a} = \mathfrak{a}_0(c) \oplus \mathfrak{a}_{1/2}(c) \oplus \mathfrak{a}_1(c)$ into the $0, \frac{1}{2}, 1$-eigenspaces of $L(c)$. One sees easily that $\dim \mathfrak{a}_1(c) = \operatorname{trace} P(c) \geq 1$. It follows that $I_1 = \{c \in I : \dim \mathfrak{a}_1(c) = 1\}$ is a closed subspace of I. If $\mathfrak{a}$ is formal real, it is clear that I_1 is just the set of primitive idempotents.

THEOREM 2.9. <u>The set I_1 of primitive idempotents in a simple formal real Jordan algebra $\mathfrak{a}$ is connected and a compact symmetric space of rank one. The assignment $\mathfrak{a} \to I_1$ establishes a one-to-one correspondence between isomorphism classes of simple formal real Jordan algebras and compact symmetric spaces of rank one</u>.

In more detail, the spaces I_1 for the different types of $\mathfrak{a}$ are given in the following table, which also summarizes some of the previous results. Here Y_1^* denoted the compact dual of the noncompact symmetric space $Y_1 = \{y \in Y(\mathfrak{a}) : \det P(y) = 1\}$ and H^* the compact dual of the halfspace $H = \mathfrak{a} \oplus \sqrt{-1}\, Y(\mathfrak{a})$.

$\mathfrak{A}$	(r,d)	Y_1^*	H^*	I_1
$\mathbb{R}$	$(1,0)$	$\{\cdot\}$	S^2	$\{\cdot\}$
$\mathbb{R}.e\oplus\mathbb{R}^{d+1}$ $(d\geq 1)$	$(2,d)$	S^{d+1}	$\tilde{M}(2,d+4;\mathbb{R})$	S^d
$\mathcal{H}(r,\mathbb{R})$ $(r\geq 3)$	$(r,1)$	A_{r-1}^R	C_r^R	$P_{r-1}(\mathbb{R})$
$\mathcal{H}(r,\mathbb{C})$ $(r\geq 3)$	$(r,2)$	$SU(r)$	$M(r,2r;C)$	$P_{r-1}(\mathbb{C})$
$\mathcal{H}(r,\mathbb{H})$ $(r\geq 3)$	$(r,4)$	A_{2r-1}^H	D_{2r}^H	$P_{r-1}(\mathbb{H})$
$\mathcal{H}(3,\mathbb{O})$	$(3,8)$	$E_{6(-26)}$	$E_{7(-25)}$	$P_2(\mathbb{O})$

Table 2

NOTES

§1 The standard facts on Hermitian symmetric spaces and bounded domains can be found in Helgason [1].

§2 The notion of a domain of positivity (also called a self-dual cone) is due to Koecher [1], [2], as is the correspondence with Jordan algebras. A generalization is the ω-domains. An exposition of the clasification of Jordan algebras can be found in Braun-Koecher [1]. Theorem 2.5 is due to Hirzebruch [1]. The Cayley transformation φ has been extensively studied and extended to all Hermitian symmetric spaces by Korányi-Wolf [1], [2]. Theorem 2.8 is taken from there. The material on primitive idempotents in Jordan algebras is due to Hirzebruch [2]. Recently, Koecher [3] found a unified way of constructing all Hermitian symmetric spaces from Jordan algebras.

BIBLIOGRAPHY

S. ARAKI

1. "On root systems and an infinitesimal classification of irreducible symmetric spaces." Jour. of Math., Osaka City Univ. 13 (1962), 1-34.

2. "On Bott-Samelson K-cycles associated with symmetric spaces." Jour. of Math., Osaka City Univ. 13 (1962), 87-133.

A. BOREL et J. DE SIEBENTHAL

1. "Les sous-groupes fermés de rang maximum des groupes de Lie clos." Comm. Math. Helv. 23 (1949), 200-221.

R. BOTT and H. SAMELSON

1. "Applications of the theory of Morse to symmetric spaces." Amer. Jour. Math. 80 (1958), 964-1028.

H. BRAUN und M. KOECHER

1. Jordan-Algebren. Springer-Verlag, Berlin-Heidelberg-New York, 1966.

É. CARTAN

1. "Sur une classe remarquable d'espaces de Riemann." Bull. Soc. Math. France 54 (1926), 214-264; 55 (1927), 114-134.

2. "Sur certaines formes riemanniennes remarquables des géométries à groupe fondamental simple." Ann. Sci. École Norm. Sup. 44 (1927), 345-467.

C. CHEVALLEY

1. Theory of Lie Groups. Vol. I. Princeton University Press, Princeton, New Jersey, 1946.

R. GODEMENT

1. Theorie des Faisceaux. Hermann, Paris, 1958.

S. HELGASON

1. Differential Geometry and Symmetric Spaces. Academic Press, New York - London, 1962.

2. "Totally geodesic spheres in compact symmetric spaces." Math. Annalen 165 (1966), 309-317.

U. HIRZEBRUCH

1. "Halbräume und ihre holomorphen Automorphismen." Math. Annalen 153 (1964), 395-417.

2. "Über Jordan-Algebren und kompakte Riemannsche symmetrische Räume vom Rang 1." Math. Z. 90 (1965), 339-354.

G. HOCHSCHILD

1. The Structure of Lie Groups. Holden-Day, San Francisco, 1965.

H. HOPF

1. "Maximale Toroide und singuläre Elemente in geschlossenen Lieschen Gruppen." Comm. Math. Helv. 15 (1942), 59-70.

H. HOPF und H. SAMELSON

1. "Ein Satz über die Wirkungsräume geschlossener Liescher Gruppen." Comm. Math. Helv. 13 (1940), 240-251.

N. IWAHORI and H. MATSUMOTO

1. "On some Bruhat decompositions and the structure of the Hecke rings of p-adic Chevalley groups." IHES, Publications Mathématiques No. 25 (1965), 237-280.

N. JACOBSON

1. Lie Algebras. Interscience Publishers, New York - London, 1962.

2. "Triality and Lie algebras of type D_4." Rend. Circ. Mat. di Palermo II, 13 (1964), 129-153.

M. KOECHER

1. "Positivitätsbereiche im R^n." Amer. J. Math. 79 (1957), 575-596.

2. Jordan Algebras and their Applications. University of Minnesota Lecture notes, 1962.

3. "Gruppen und Lie-Algebren rationaler Funktionen." To appear.

A. KORÁNYI and J. A. WOLF

1. "Realization of Hermitian symmetric spaces as generalized half-planes." Ann. of Math. 81 (1965), 265-288.

2. "Generalized Cayley transformations of bounded symmetric domains." Amer. J. Math. 87 (1965), 899-939.

W. G. LISTER

1. "A structure theory of Lie triple systems." Trans. Amer. Math. Soc. 72 (1952), 217-242.

O. LOOS

1. "Spiegelungsräume und homogene symmetrische Mannigfaltigkeiten." Dissertation, München, 1966.

2. "Spiegelungsräume und homogene symmetrische Räume." Math. Z. 99 (1967), 141-170.

S. MACLANE

1. Homology. Springer Verlag, Berlin-Göttingen-Heidelberg, 1963.

J. NAGATA

1. Modern Dimension Theory. North Holland Publishing Company, Amsterdam, 1965.

I. SATAKE

1. "On representations and compactifications of symmetric Riemannian spaces." Ann. of Math. 71 (1960), 77-110.

R. D. SCHAFER

1. Introduction to Non-Associative Algebras. Academic Press, New York, 1966.

J.-P. SERRE

1. Algèbres de Lie Semi-Simple Complexes. W. A. Benjamin, New York - Amsterdam, 1966.

J. DE SIEBENTHAL

1. "Sur les groupes de Lie compacts non connexes." Comm. Math. Helv. 31 (1956), 41-89.

E. H. SPANIER

1. Algebraic Topology. McGraw-Hill, New York, 1966.

E. STIEFEL

1. "Über eine Beziehung zwischen geschlossenen Lie'schen Gruppen und diskontinuierlichen Bewegungsgruppen euklidischer Räume und ihre Anwendung auf die Aufzählung der einfachen Lie'schen Gruppen." Comm. Math. Helv. 14 (1942), 350-380.

J. TITS

1. "Sur les constantes de structure et le théorème d'existence des algèbres de Lie semi-simples." IHES, Publications Mathématiques, No. 31 (1966), 21-58.
2. Tabellen zu den einfachen Lie Gruppen und ihren Darstellungen. Springer-Verlag, Berlin-Heidelberg-New York, 1967.

R. E. WALDE

1. "Composition algebras and exceptional Lie algebras." Dissertation, Berkeley, 1967.

J. A. WOLF

1. Spaces of Constant Curvature. McGraw-Hill, New York, 1967.

INDEX